CUL-DE-SAC ANGELS

CUL-DE-SAC ANGELS

Michelle Emily Garcia

Michelle Emily Garcia

ISBN: 978-0-578-86016-9 (Paperback)

Edited by Michelle Emily Garcia

Front Cover Art by Michelle Emily Garcia

Back Cover Art by Skyler Vada Taube

Author Photo by Alyssa Duong

Printed by Lightning Source LLC in the United States of America.

First paperback edition April 2021.

www.mooopsy.com

for my greatest teachers,
Mom and Dad

Contents

Introduction

In true writer fashion, I am sitting by the window of my apartment bedroom struggling to find the adequate words to preface my first "tapestry" of original work. I've been dismissing this section, cripplingly self-conscious of the notion that, by the time your eyes reach these words, my writing will no longer be entirely my own. It is fifty degrees on the cusp of April, two o'clock in the afternoon, and I am twenty-one years old. Lately, my mind has been plagued by a cyclical sort of existential anxiety—of what corner of the world I'll occupy in just a few short months, my lack of remotely cohesive post-graduation plans, which relationships I'll take with me or tragically lose to time's unfair embrace.

This is the essence of *Cul-e-sac Angels*, I think: a culmination of the anxieties and traumas and revelations I've been blessed (or cursed?) enough to confront. There is a part of me that will always belong to the '70s-style, residential neighborhoods of my childhood universe where my "firsts" survive. Another part remains forever tethered to the quaint college town where I blissfully consumed every blurry minute of the three most formative years of my life. There are even fragments of myself left behind in my parents' native Philippines. I've still never been, though the language flows endlessly through my blood. I consist of so many places I will never be able to abandon completely. We all are. We leave sticky fingerprints in faraway places.

I don't know where you call home, which God or lack thereof you worship, which flag has earned your allegiance, or how many times you have fallen in love. But mine? These pages contain portraits of the wicked and wonderful lives I've lived, stories from both inside and outside of the cul-de-sac. I've built a home here, and you're welcome to kick off your shoes and keep me company. In fact, please do. Conversing with the wallpaper can be too lonely to bear.

Cul-?e-sac Angels is divided into six distinct chapters that overlap and intertwine.

"MYTHOLOGICAL MOVEMENTS" comes first, as we begin with my obsession with nostalgia. I often joke to my friends that "I've never gotten over anything, not a single thing, ever." It's comically absurd, but some semblance of truth actually exists behind that hyperbole. My mind has always been drawn to the retrospect, and I have developed a habit of digging up the dead and buried without even realizing it. I miss *so much*. I am constantly wrestling with these cosmic changes that break my foolishly idealistic heart in microscopic ways every day. I romanticize a world still untainted by the online sphere, when human interaction felt more physical and genuine, before the age of ironic disconnect—you name it—I am deeply affected by these colossal paradigm shifts. In this section, you'll also be able to travel through a disorganized mosaic of memories, the edges and curves of a life I can barely trace after years of disillusionment. Crisp observations from three-year-old eyes, from my townhouse bedroom (fun fact: I repeat "bubblegum pink walls" far too many times in this book), from awkward middle school dances, from my first year away at college. Many are memories I've tried to forget, visions of past lives that stung like hell the day I finally mustered enough courage to relive them on paper. But, like all writers, I am an archaeologist. I can't help but excavate, never capturing enough.

"STORIES BY GHOSTS" covers heartbreak in all of its forms. For a while, this chapter was titled "GHOST STORIES," and then "STORIES OF GHOSTS." But I later realized, in the process of rereading these personal chronicles of deep love and even deeper loss, that these stories were technically co-written, in a bizarre way, since I only played the role of *one* character in my shared love stories. There was always a second party, and that person is just as present in this raw collage of recollections as I am. It's just that I happened to be the one to pick up the pen first. "STORIES BY GHOSTS" captures an unfair yearning for something lost—to time, distance, a third party, etcetera—sometimes temporarily, but oftentimes forever. These narratives are unfiltered, tender, and private. I've laid out the gritty details for you: the shapes and textures of adoring a person intensely and without rationality— and still I have no shame. I've been slowly learning to view this variety of pain as *privilege*, as something sacred. I've mingled my soul with other people's souls: some of them too beautiful to bear, some far removed from beauty. But to experience heartbreak means you have loved wholly and without pretense, that you have poured your matter into someone else's matter and *all of it mattered*. And what is that, if not holy?

"SHAPES OF DEVOTION" is next. These are love poems. Watercolor portraits of romantic love, mostly, but also distinct variations of love: platonic friendships, familial comfort, even grief—which I almost put into the former category until I decided that mourning is just another dialect of love. To love and be loved is an experience that cannot be replicated or even adequately described. I'm still not sure how to characterize this chapter. Maybe you can for me. These are simply my impressions, illusions, confessions, and musings. I am spellbound and charmed and fueled by love. Read and take what you need. These are snapshots of goodness I've been lucky enough to call my own.

The fourth section, "WHISPERED EXPLOSIONS," is a chapter that centers around apocalyptic thinking. I wrote and compiled this entire section during the year 2020, which can ultimately be summed up by various evils: the seemingly never-ending COVID-19 pandemic, systemic racism and heinous acts of injustice, corrupt politics, growing climate disruptions, and more. I wrote most of these poems in my iPhone Notes app, confined in my childhood bedroom after being swiftly removed from the real world for months. They're largely unrevised and in original form; fitting, I think, for times this wild and uncharted. Strangely, though, I've always been socially distanced in my head, as a choice. At first, sitting with myself in silence was more than bearable—but *ideal*. Eventually, though, I began haunting myself, my own body. "WHISPERED EXPLOSIONS" is at once a dystopian landscape and a newsreel. This is the story of what we all survived in a year.

Oh, "SELF AS WAR." The most vulnerable chapter by far. Here, I blend fiction, poetry, and nonfiction in ways that may be unsettling or uncomfortable to read. Peruse with caution. This chapter covers subjects such as sexual assault, suicide, depictions of mental illness, and what it means to be a survivor of events you still can't bring yourself to talk about directly. I've lost so much of myself in the countless hours I spent facedown in the grass, in faithless moments of reckless behavior, bruised and cradled in the arms of bad people. Some have asked, "Why publish internal torment?" My response: as a form of catharsis, of shedding skin, of clearing space for goodness and drawing the curtains for good. This is my way of celebrating that.

And at last, we make it back home again, to "RECLAMATION"—except this particular home looks a little different. *Cul-␣e-sac Angels* concludes with a full-circle air of hope I want you to experience for yourself. I won't spell it out for you. Go ahead. Peer in.

This is *Cul-␣e-sac Angels*, my firstborn, and I am so blessed to share her with you.

Forever yours and with all sincerity,

Michelle

I

MYTHOLOGICAL MOVEMENTS

Strange Paradise

I thirst for strawberry summers, my nine-year-old body
outstretched on the grassy slope of our front yard.
It is noon and I smell of residential pool chlorine
and not nearly enough sunscreen. The world is good
and I am aware of this, shoulders burnt pink enough
to start a fire, sky so cloudless I imagine dipping my toes
into it, finding no bottom, and sinking into some strange
paradise. But I blink and there I am on my back again,
and the mailwoman has arrived with nothing important,
just grocery store coupons, a water bill, and a wave hello,
and I wave hello back, because I am nine summers young
and I believe in the kindness of cul-de-sac angels and that I,
freckled and peachy, play a part in a good, good world.

Bedroom Collection 1/2

I.

Chipped bubblegum walls, nail-sized hole in the ceiling
from the Christmas morning Dad hung a princess canopy
over the quilted twin bed and I, being just five earthly years,
nearly died of rejoicing. There's a snow globe collection
(*Kansas City, The Big Apple, some Canadian province*
with a funny name) hidden next to stacks of early 2000s
DVDs dusted over by eighteen years of girlhood magic. From that
window I used to watch the tulip poplar rooted in our yard
blossom and shed like an honorable prostitute. I remember
when she finally succumbed to the kind of malignant cancer
ancient trees inherit and the bad men in trucks came to uproot
and dethrone her and kidnap my only friend away. That day
they left an abyss in the ground still so terribly unnatural that
even now our grass only grows deep green around it, as if forever
stunted by what unspeakable crime (*the breaking of my heart*)
had been committed there.

II.

                                I want to tell you another story
about that window and the foreign flavors it offered me. The
awkward stage of my thirteenth spring I perched there with Dad's
pocket-sized binoculars to observe, with my freckled girl friend,
the boy with the floppy brown almost-mullet playing Shirts
versus Skins on the sloping field by the middle school we attended.
We'd just watch, illiterate in the male species, giggling through
tight braces like schoolgirls because that's exactly what we were.
Three years later a boy with another name stood beneath the window

as valiant and hormonal as Shakespeare's Romeo and "promposed" to me with pink roses in his hand by reading poetry from computer paper written in Crayola marker. I said yes yes yes (*an♦ ran like ma♦ ♦ownstairs to thank him for letting me play his blushing Juliet*).

III.

In that room I grew to be small and jealous and in love
with worlds apart from it. That place is now a portal
to a dimension where I was once innocent enough to believe
in simple things: bedtime prayers, the oak desk permanently
stained with yellow acrylic paint, dog-eared books (*Sylvia Plath's
Ariel, my a♦olescent journals, The Velveteen Rabbit, The Nutcracker Ballet,
an unrea♦ copy of Anna Karenina*) tucked in secret nooks, Polaroids
of now-strangers ruined by terrible exposure, names
of pop star crushes I scrawled on the wall behind my mattress.
Nothing vaguely unholy ever happened there, in that
suburban dollhouse of a room where the inimitable smells
of summer (*neighbor's barbecue, bug spray, si♦ewalk chalk,
chlorine an♦ backyar♦ sprinkler*) wafted in, and I took it all in,
inhaled every atom of it, because I was young and because
there was nothing better to do and no one better to be.

Fragrant Flashbacks

Certain scents—magnolia, freshly washed linen,
dish soap bubbles in the sink—are thieves of peace.
My first love's coconut deodorant, tasteless cafeteria
food from the hospice where I watched my grandma
shrink from the cancer that killed her, the bedsheets
of a boy who just wanted an excuse to wash them.
When love fades to past tense, when the letters stop
coming, when I reach out to touch you and only
feel cold air running through my fingers—I inhale
as much of it as I can. Cinnamon. Mom's signature
perfume. These odd specifics, particulars, fragrant
flashbacks. Memories float within motes of dust.

As Kids

We were smart. Cul-de-sac geniuses
in hand-me-down bermuda shorts.
My cousins and I, we were raised by
the Backstreet Boys on the boombox,
Kodak disposables, scraped knees.
I am nostalgic now, for that textbook
Americana, 25-cent lemonade stands
and yard sales where we'd bid farewell to
outgrown tricycles and pink dollhouses.

We could braid, too. French and Dutch
and other styles we'd invent on the fine,
blonde hair of our American Girl dolls.
I remember wanting hair like that—
gold like the movie stars' on the posters
Scotch-taped to my bubblegum walls.

Reduced to mythology now, practically
fiction, the only leftovers still remaining
are the lives we abandoned under plastic
sleeves in the albums we only flip through
when we come home for Christmas break.

We were unmanufactured. Scruffy, wild,
grass-stained and privileged. Sidewalk
rulers, gods and monsters of blanket forts
and summer sprinklers and shared family.

Sometimes I close my eyes and it's 2004
and we're in the hammock, just me and my
cousins, and we're a sticky heap of August,
banana-scented sunscreen, and tenderness.

It Is August 28, 2004

And I'm a monster with a milk mustache
stirring Froot Loops to make the colors run.

Today is a good day.

Today I will arrange my plastic figurines
in a summoning circle. Ronald McDonald,
Snow White, Winnie-the-Pooh, Spider-Man.
I like it when my best friends hold hands.

I also like summer.

Summer means haircuts by Mom in the kitchen,
streamers and training wheels and even a bell
that Dad installed for me to call the neighbor's
cats. There is no need to dream if I live in one.

I have everything.

I am almost five and I am scared of fireworks
and the big dogs down the street and one day
I want to be an astronaut but won't actually
go to space because space is big for someone
small like me. But enough about one day,
because today I will just dance in the sprinkler.

I know everything there is to know
about everything worth knowing.

Like how you shouldn't open your eyes
in the public pool or they will sting bad.
And how crayons don't taste the way
they look. And how sometimes people
fall asleep and we cry about it and when
you hold their hand they don't hold back.

I don't like it.

But I like that today is the last Saturday of summer
and I'm not in space. I'm four. I'm home.

And I am so proud to be loved like this.

I Owe Everything I Am

to scraped knees and fireflies swarming in glasses
under pencil-poked cling wrap and OshKosh B'gosh
overalls and mushroom cuts for my two-year-old hair
the geometry perfected by my mother on the tile-floored
bathroom of our townhouse. My cousins and I used to
choreograph dances for our families every Christmas
Eve without fail. I owe everything I am to the Sony
camcorders that captured our basement recitals.
To every couple that picked me to play flower girl
though I ripped petals and threw temper tantrums at
every wedding I walked. That taught me grace and
I owe everything I am to whatever taught me that.
My father used to pitch nylon tents in the living
room so I could pretend to be a runaway. I hauled
all of my Beanie Babies and pretend picnic food
and plastic dinosaurs and lined them all up so I'd never
feel lonely or imaginary hungry, even for a fugitive
on the run. One day Mom and I helped Dad paint
our entire white-walled home like the inside of
a kaleidoscope. *Dan•elion yellow kitchen salmon •ining
room lilac •en lime green hallway malaya re• front •oor.*
It was only until I was older that I understood
the significance of such fumes. I owe everything I am
to the ones who made sure I would grow up in a castle
of color, fenced in by dreaming, inside a safe life where
I couldn't owe anyone anything but my best. To pink
dollhouses and Perler beads under hot irons and Mom's
sewing fingers that could always mend the rips on my

tattered teddy bears and accidental tears on ballet costumes
so nothing bad would ever happen or ever could. I owe
everything to everything I've had since the beginning.
I was born into the right world and I owe everything to that.

Anatomy of a Girl on Fire

On the top shelf of the closet in my childhood bedroom is my heart in a shoebox. I hoard memories because they are the closest replicas I have to a life that can still hold its own shape. When people ask about my past I wish I could take them home to rummage through the cardboard walls, to pour out its contents in search of something palpable, something like me.

You'd know more about me if you knew the types of things I choose to keep.

There's a sepia photograph of my mother as a child, torn around the edges as if harvested from a larger picture lost to time. A pocket music box I purchased from a kitschy shop in Vienna, Austria that still plays "Eine kleine Nachtmusik" when you crank the metal handle. A realistic cat figurine with faux fur I took from a hallway cart in my grandmother's nursing home before she died of cancer (that probably belonged to someone next door who died just days before she did). A magnetic key card I accidentally stole from the Hotel Chopin in Sochaczew, Poland that I must've thrown into my suitcase as we hurried out before dawn to catch a flight back home. Tickets to magical places: *Les Misérables* at the National Theatre, the *Angels in America* production held at my university, Lorde's *Melo•rama* world tour where I mourned over my adolescence under fluorescent green lights, a personalized walk-through of the Vatican Museum, the crumbling Rocca Maggiore castle in Assisi (where I got stuck in a spiral staircase in the tallest tower), a Lufthansa plane ticket to Rome from when I was sixteen years old and a world traveler. Clutter that normal people would throw away in a heartbeat: a suspiciously perfect cube of rubber I found in the grass after my senior year homecoming game and just never threw away, a gravy-stained receipt that a former coworker used to write a note of encouragement to me—*Hi Michelle! You got it!*—when I worked the front line of my minimum wage food service job scooping potatoes and turkey for a university-wide Thanksgiving feast. My middle and high school ID cards, playbills of the musicals where I took center stage (*Shrek! The Wiz! The A••ams Family!*), a tin container of unwrapped soap that, to me, can only be described using the word "Christmas." A folded letter from my dear friend Julie from our first semester of college, dozens of orchestra medals from when I was first violin concertmaster, proof I've lived a life I chose for myself: a postcard from Wexford, Pennsylvania when I first visited my love in his own city, a stamped slip to ride the Duquesne Incline in Downtown Pittsburgh, a lanyard from Virginia Tech's freshman orientation back when my world felt brand new, blurry Polaroids of people I can't call friends anymore, the first poem I ever felt proud of writing: "A Time Will Come," written on a manual typewriter in the winter of seventh grade. Photographs of various eras: prom night, sitting with my friends in a sunflower field, group shots of a Catholic retreat I attended three separate times even though, at the time, I couldn't tell you I believed in God at all. A brochure to the Sylvia Plath exhibit at the National Portrait Gallery where I stood very still for an hour, basking in the relics of my idol. My high school graduation announcement. A tiny jar of gold leaf flakes from Santa's elves in 2004 that came with a note of warning: "Do not open. Water will turn you into a frog." My dad still finds that one clever. A bucket list I typewrote before I turned thirteen: *Marry the love of my life. Take a selfie with a shark. Try a weir• ice cream flavor (like pickle!!!). Sky•ive. Gra•uate high school with flying colors.* I smile to myself before crossing that last one off. It feels good. 70% of people with my mental illness do not end up graduating. I think of the girl who wrote that, the girl with all of this *stuff* in her mind with no place to put it. I imagine her smiling back, proud of me.

How I Know There's a Part of Me That Still Feels

When my father paints over the bubblegum pink walls of my childhood bedroom, I have to look away. It's as if we are burying a living thing, ignoring the rise and fall of a heaving chest, hiding a fresh corpse from eager scavengers. I think of everything that particular shade of pink has seen. Wild cousin laughter and fumbled guitar chords and futile first attempts at love poetry. Bad boyfriends and pretty good ones and ghosts of a younger body hunched over a sticky-keyed typewriter. That shade of pink knows me more than I do, has witnessed every slip into madness and every rare moment of peace. But there's a flickering like grace even in the undoing. There's an air of calm in the deconstruction of a past that no longer flatters a frame like mine.

I buried a friend today.

I loved her but it was time.

In So Many Ways I Am Still Fifteen

in so many ways I am still fifteen / I don't want to give anything up / these sugar sweet saccharine days / still L'Oréal lipstick in Cinnamon Toast / still a body doused in Bath & Body Works' A Thousand Wishes / still it burns the nostrils like liquid fire / still my very first kiss under a blanket of stars / still a bad driver, wheels slamming into the curb every time / still skeptical at Sunday mass, pinching my thigh to believe in how real it burns / still this dense suburban air is the only air I've ever known / because in so many ways I am still fifteen / not wanting to give anything up / still shaking out of fear in high school bathrooms / still sporting chipped fingernail polish / just take it off already damn it / why do I / still hold onto things that have already had their time? / still my baby pink bedroom / still the secrets I can't even tell God / I can feel Him listening through the walls / still I doubt anyone would ever save me / I don't even know if I would have saved me / back then at least / but I do it every day now / in so many ways / in so many ways / in so many ways / because I have to! / because what would Jesus do? / I'm still not sure / but nowadays I find myself smiling at me / yes / that me / still fifteen / still unable to give anything up / and with hands folded in prayer / she smiles back / did you hear that? / she smiles back.

Generation Why

None of us remember much of September 11, 2001 except that we could still sit upright in bathtubs while our mothers lathered our hair in twirls of Johnson's baby shampoo. It was a day of soap bubbles and her tears and wondering without language why she shut off the Barney VHS tape to watch two buildings melt into earth as if they had never been there to begin with. To be born in the finite and contestable space between Y and Z means that nothing about our childhood is definitive. Nothing, one could argue, is authentically ours. We had patterns to follow. Our baby photos were the last to be stored behind plastic photo album sleeves, developed from Kodak disposable camera film, before the birth of digital. But we were not the first. I remember holding reels of pale orange negatives up to the car window on the way to the drugstore and finding my whole life confined in a world of shadow. My childhood was Firecracker Popsicles and plastic Kens and Kellys and Barbies with mismatched clothes and French-braiding American Girl doll hair until my fingers lost feeling. We weaved friendship bracelets with rainbow craft store thread and traded Silly Bandz at recess, a thing we invented, but still relished in our Easy-Bake ovens passed down from the '90s. So much of our joys were hand-me-downs and borrowed clothes and copied fads. We didn't trend Scrunchies; we stole them from our older cousins. It was the age after the world lost innocence. It was the age before the beginning of the end. We were simple and suburban, products of scraped knees and Heelys and the second Bush presidency. When I think of being little I don't remember screens or upgrades or this newfangled hatred that permeates through all of it. When I think of being little I remember feeling big. I made Play-Doh castles and carried my purple CD player to the corner ice cream shop. I wore mosquito repellent as perfume and measured my worth by how many laps on the sidewalk I could make on my Razor scooter. I lost count at twenty-six. I think about it now and there had to be a last time. There was a day we traded Pokémon cards for sitting on our phones at sleepovers and our View-Master 3D stereoscopes for Instagram filters. None of the new is evil or bad or wrong; it's just not the same. Back then we all wore shirts we tie-dyed in our backyards with our aunts. My mother tells me that after I was born everyone thought the world would end. '99 was dying, the Times Square ball would drop for Y2K, and all of America assumed apocalypse. But no, we're still here; some of us, at least. There was a last time, though. A last time life felt real.

I Cried Today Because I Thought About

Christmas Eve, all of my cousins sitting criss-cross applesauce on the basement floor, bodies covered in wrapping paper from a night of being spoiled to death. That's just how it is in our family: we're kids forever, even though most of us will probably marry this decade or have babies or both. I'm the youngest and I'm twenty. Still, it's like we never aged past elementary school. I'm remembering how we'd complain every holiday, blinded by camera flashes, because our Asian moms just *ha*₊ to capture every small moment, every new present we'd pull from each individual gift bag to reveal, even stopping to pose us like porcelain dolls. *3, 2, 1—smile!* And we'd groan through our teeth and roll our eyes at how pointless it was. Another one for the album! Didn't we already have enough albums?

It's the togetherness that I miss most: growing up a little more each year in a thousand different ways, yet always finding each other on Christmas Eve, catching up on the couch over plates heaping with crispy egg rolls and noodles. And then *Line up! Line up! It's picture time!* How we'd all look at each other and sigh loudly, because we knew that it'd take at least half an hour to get that perfect shot in front of the Christmas tree, the one that would make our mothers—and Facebook—happy.

The things I would do to be there right now—touching, cackling at the silliness of it all, eating together, no tragedy. It's the only perfect world I still have left in my mind.

Moral of the story: there are never enough albums.

4:06 PM

I took my first breath then.

My mother can still resurrect that afternoon as crisp as new.

One of those perfect November days, sixty-four degrees

and cloudy with a chance of hope. That sacred autumn cool

where all there is to do is wait for something to happen.

So that's just what she did. She waited for me like prayer.

For years, I'd wait for the exact moment she waited for

to blow out my candles. I couldn't even consider myself

an entire year older until the minute hand reached the time

I was born into this new world of being *aughter,* 4:06 PM,

baby pink in my father's arms, no longer just i*ea,*

or mere *possibility,* or even *the *ream come true,*

she will be born healthy, she will be born girl,

until the instance of magic

I felt her hands for the first time

and became not just *aughter,* but *theirs.*

Sometimes, even on days that are not my birthday,

just normal drowsy afternoons with nothing left to do

but wait for the sound of something sweet to fill the air,

I just breathe. All over again, like prayer—

taking it all in

as if for the first time.

I Was Five and I Knew

I knew everything there is to know
by the time I turned five. Like *rain—*

it is for swaddling your bones in quilts
and listening, motionless,
nothing else,
just listening.

If you do so close enough, it sounds a lot
like how the idea of God makes some people
believe in things unseen. I knew then
that I was made for blind faith.

The sky is an open book. It will whisper
its origin stories and saturate your shoulders
with its wisdom if you lean into it,
if you look up.

I was five and I knew
that nothing else could ever teach me more.

Perfect Interruptions

When I want to feel young again, I dust off my guitar and perform to the walls like a bored ten-year-old passing time during the summer's first power outage. There was nothing to do whenever it happened, other than the obvious, of course: peering through the window on my tiptoes to see if the neighborhood across the woods had gotten its lights turned back on yet. I sucked at waiting. So I'd sculpt my delicate fingers strong enough to barre chords—usually dissonant sounds at first—and then something close to music. It was pitch black and I sat at the foot of my parents' empty bed teaching myself the alien mechanics of strumming, synchronizing my voice with the *own-* *own-up-* *own.* Time takes on a peculiar shape when all you can do is pass it. It's as if you can feel yourself getting old, sitting in the stillness, baking in mid-July fever. I could feel the indifference of those bedroom walls, sweat pooling at the nape of my neck, and I felt my age. I was one decade young yet I was old enough to feel it—to be a small thing lit up by the rage of something new. Since then, I don't think I've ever felt that indisputably alive. For a moment, summer held her breath and I did too, saving that melodrama for myself.

Ode to Strange Fixations

At ten, it was eating, not picking,
the soft flesh around my fingertips.
I'd do it on the bus to fifth grade
and then wonder why no cute boy
wanted to hold my hand, pitiful
cannibal. At fifteen, it was a boy
who held more than just my hand,
but my heart, aflame, in his pocket.
At twenty, it is perfume and candles
and houseplants. My windowsill
brims with succulents and seasonal
mums and I tend to them like small
children. It's the end of the world
but playing the role of careful mother
offers the almost-believable illusion
that we are not as doomed as we feel.

Praise be to the things that grow.

Praise be to the obsessions we grow
with and then out of, our dead skin
and dead names and overwatered
plants, still clinging to life somehow.

Bildungsroman

I grew up on Sunday night youth group playing Sardines behind the Catholic parish chapel under suburban stars. We used to intentionally hide in storage closets so we could sit with our crushes in dark stillness, bodies innocently pressed against ceiling-high stacks of metal folding chairs. It was the age of giddy purity. My coming-of-age story was written in brick red drugstore lipstick and thrifted prom dresses I wore to my first real boyfriend's homeschool parties. It was the age of Sylvia Plath's *The Bell Jar* and Arctic Monkeys and baby pink Converse high-tops muddied by hometown soil. Of uneven side bangs cut with safety scissors and sucking in my stomach at the ballet barre in that pale yellow room with mirrored walls. Back then I believed in everything and nothing. I wanted to be sought after but not seen. I was a good girl pining for faraway cities and freedom from my seventeenth year. I wrote my college applications in free verse poetry and shrugged my shoulders at every rejection letter. I trained my mouth to memorize the vocabulary of bad girls. At the time I envisioned my future self finally content in a New York apartment, some prestigious writing school, marrying someone who would teach me to outgrow my sweetness. Someone who would teach me how to live. I never quite reached those dreams but in retrospect they were good to have. I covered every inch of my bedroom wall with magazine cutouts of body parts I found beautiful. Elbows and lips and glittery eyes. I didn't know it then but this was my attempt to assemble myself a body I felt safe in. I can still feel my heart racing, crouching behind the back door of the church, half-hoping to be found so the game would end.

Still Walking Home

I am dreaming of a certain place and time and it is neither here nor now. Tonight, I am eighteen again. Lorde's *Melodrama* overwhelms the wires of my headphones as I walk home from campus's most hated dining hall with a carryout box of lukewarm Chinese noodles. It's October, and the leaves have yet to turn, and it's just rained in the typical Southwest Virginia fashion: sudden downpour followed by perfect, holy stillness. I'm making every effort to step gracefully into every puddle, rubber rain boots tiptoeing across the wet, starlit pavement. Wandering alone at night is a kind of prayer, I realize at this moment. Loneliness is perfect company; it'll talk back to you if you let it. Here in the blue, rolling mountains, I am capable of dreaming in a way my retired suburbia could never permit. The energy always sickened me: gridlock, depressed commuters, pollution of the air and mind. It's just different here. Tomorrow I'll call my mom and tell her I want to get my PhD in poetry someday because my most intimidating professor told me I had a terrifying knack for unleashing beauty. I'll take the transit bus to nowhere with a new friend of mine and let her convince me to adopt a betta fish for my dorm room. I'll send a handwritten letter to the boy I adored and left behind for a new world unfit for the two of us to remain tethered at the hip. I don't know what I'll end up writing yet. *I miss you* sounds too much like *I miss home*, as if the sentiments are interchangeable, which I cannot say with integrity. Maybe I'll ramble on about how I'm trying to become a vegetarian because I care too deeply about the cows I pass when I stroll through the golden pastures, or that I've been sucking at making it to Sunday mass, or that I'm letting myself be impulsive with someone who *wants* (not loves) me because no one's here to tell me I shouldn't mess with hands as greedy as his. In my head I'm still walking home, inebriated by dense autumn air and life itself. I know the noodles will be awful. But it doesn't matter, because I'm turning nineteen in three weeks, and I'm seriously considering getting my nose pierced like the cool girls in my literature classes, and tonight my loneliness does more than just talk back—it sings.

Bedroom Collection 2/2

I.

Damp air, mold and mildew, paper-thin facades leaving
nothing to the imagination. Even with the door locked
and secured by electronic keypad prone to malfunction
I knew exactly what so-and-so did last Friday night with
an upperclassman she met while inebriated at one of the
more notorious fraternity houses. Alpha something or
other. I didn't even have to ask, I heard. In that room
we left the windows gaping wide in the dead of winter.
The air never moved, only churned like a sick stomach.

II.

T and I weren't really friends but then we were
and then we weren't and then we finally were, for
real the last time. In our corners, snapshots of past
lives. Boyfriends. High school theatre performances.
Smiling faces of hearts we had to leave behind. How
comical, what humidity and homesickness and hardly
a 10×10 expanse of cheap tile floor can do to two girls.
We grew insane in there as our photos, Scotch-taped
and secured, plummeted from the sweating wall. Sad fate.
Nothing stuck. It was a home we tried to make a home
but never really became a home, no matter how many
times we rearranged the furniture at 3 A.M. in hopes of
changing the energy of that blessed, cursed lack of space.

III.

When she left for good I stayed behind and felt
strange inside, the room barren and stripped of noise,
of Kacey Musgraves's *Golden Hour* on loop from her side of
the room, the wafting scent of burnt cookies from the kitchen
next door, the volleyball court view usually obstructed by
window box fans, our end-of-day talking half-asleep about
who we ran into, the clumps of hair we found in the sticky
communal showers, the rowdy boys down the hall always
yelling about unimportant things, everything and nothing.

IV.

Suddenly it was May and the world smelled of flowers
blooming in sidewalk cracks and it was time to leave forever.
Out came the rags and the floor cleaner and away went the
remnants of my first year, clothes folded and crammed back
into the car trunk they hailed from. It was the end of spring
and my soul twinged, having left behind the first place I ever
dreamt of forgetting. We were there and then we weren't.

V.

I pass it sometimes. Familiar limestone and brick. Still,
it's not the same. We no longer haunt. No more of our tears
fall within the cement walls of the sacred profane, no more
constant hum, heat never rising, song of summer stuck
in the throat. That damp air belongs to someone else now.

VI.

It changed us, though.
It changed us.

Montage

You know, the smell after rain in the suburbs
is perfect for dancing barefoot in the backyard.

This is an indisputable fact of my universe—
a truth I know like the back of my own hand,
my first language, a special kind of mother tongue.

I have memorized that, every April without fail,
dandelions populate the cracks in the sidewalk
leading to our front door. How I used to pick them,
filling my fists with that tug and pull, all of that bright
yellow weed overflowing my mother's vases,
bookmarking the pages of half-finished chapters,
sunshine spilling over everywhere I dared to put it.

You know, things grow back there,
in that place (less place, more memory now)
I call home, where a small child still runs,
excavating, uprooting, part-time archaeologist
and full-time preserver of beauty.

It's true. Things really grow back there.
Like dandelions, thunderstorms,
and backyard waltzes with first loves long gone.

Girls do, too—ones like me,
with small hands and big dreams,
always reaching for something to pull from the earth.

If the Good Old Days Are Gone for Good

that's fine, I guess—I've had my share of magic. I've picked wild violets from the nooks and crannies of my backyard creek and barefoot-chased shooting stars to the end of my cul-de-sac universe. I've been nine years young with a heartbeat racing faster than the time slipping through my fingers. How my cup overflows. *Dear Diary or whoever happens to be read-ing this (IF SO, BEGONE!)*, I'd write years later, drunk on new feelings in a giddy July. *I'm in love, I'm so in love, too far in love I coul♦ ♦ie!* I documented, ending the entry by practicing my first name paired with his, marrying us on paper, the loops in my cursive stretching for eternity. It's funny, when you're old enough to drive but still can't cast your own ballot, how you swear on everything you are (indigo nail polish, horrible homemade dye jobs, punk music through a bedroom door slammed shut) that you were the first to invent love. I believed it, too. That's the cute part. I remember the day I stopped. But if the good old days are gone for good, it's alright with me. I've dizzy-danced in grocery store aisles. I've touched my lips to the wrong ones. And I might not be the inventor of love (or really any-thing at all), but damn

do I get close with you.

Luddite

Before there were screens we were magic.
Before we started crossing streets with faces
glued to glass, before we began seeking out
love in Google searches, *14,580,000,000*
results (0.68 secon∙s) but never one exact
enough to capture the whole of it. I miss
being part of a world that loved me back,
a living piece of its anatomy, apart from
this instantaneous, delirious, nauseating
madness. I remember when I was young,
using my hands. Kneading bread with
bare palms, dough collapsing under my
weight, holy labor. And later, plucking
tomatoes from the vine, beads of sweat
collecting at the hairline, nothing to
preserve the moment but that feeling
of worthiness, that my shoulders, *mine,*
my own, had been chosen by the sun
to be kissed like that. I can't remember
the last time my hands moved that
gently, assembling and dismantling
the invisible frame of reality. Know this.

I once touched the bones of this world.
I scattered fingerprints on real things.

Nesting Doll

I store every small life I've lived inside of me like a nesting doll,
layer by layer, each a dreamy variation of the next. Outermost:
linen sheets, the warm glow of summer painting my bare back,
patchouli and vetiver on my wrists. This is the one I wear now.

Crack me open. Peer in. You'll find a starry universe of becoming.

The next layer—I could never be ashamed of it. It is painted
in the colors of my hometown: the scent of fenced-in barbecues
at twilight, my first love's laughter, anger at God in church pews.
Here, I wear fishnets and write about needing to scream in a town
that would never forgive me if I did. I am untethered, hardly there.

Keep going. There is endless goodness within. You will find me
in patent leather ballet shoes, fingertips stained from art class,
innocent enough to believe in the wickedness of calling someone
stupid. I take care of earthworms and I'll sing every song I know
over voicemails to my parents' friends. I pray with my eyes closed.

It's strange to me—that you will only ever touch the shell I wear
now, that you only know me by the perfume I wear, the presence
of my laughter, and twenty years of stories still tragically untold.
Just patchouli and vetiver, sun on my shoulder blades, and skin.

The Things That Live in My Head

Eucalyptus, undiscovered alphabets, stygian blue,
the scent of my middle school crush's laundry detergent,
metaphors real enough to keep in my palms, milk baths,
the day my grandma couldn't remember my name,
dead acquaintances and Instagram posts in their honor,
the calluses on my heels from when I used to dance,
a certain girl I secretly loved, fish I buried in the backyard,
your smile on a street corner, a poster with my name on it,
and a strange, unshakable feeling of coming home.

To Old Friends Under Halcyon Skies

Out of all of the ones we made, there's one memory with a bite so deep I can never ignore it. It was late at night and we were walking the footpaths that lace the farmland behind my apartment complex. Sober and basking in cool summer air, textbook mountain weather, I remember our laughter waking up our microscopic corner of the world. Horses stood still behind the fences, gawking at our foolishness. The moon tinted our faces pale purple. Magnolia, or something of the sort, moved slowly through the air when we did. We danced under starlight without considering what we looked like: how clumsy our bodies, how awkward our geometry. I remember thinking to myself, in that precious moment stolen straight from a coming-of-age comedy, *I hope this never ends.*

But it did. And that's alright, right?

I've been thinking about that a lot recently. Maybe it's because I haven't seen a single soul in weeks. All I can do is dwell on the dead and buried past. It's not even about how it all came undone anymore; it's about everything it was *before* the coming undone. The shared playlists and midnight drives and drunken piggyback rides and group chats filled with brainless chaos. Inside jokes communicated with just an eyebrow raise, sending us into hysterics at the most inappropriate times, during sleepy lectures in the classes we hated. All of that seems so big in comparison to the horrible finale, as explosive as it was: the mean words exchanged, the hateful silence, the traumatic unraveling. It makes the worst fight seem so juvenile. If I could take back some of the words I said when I was hurt, I would. *Know that.* Maybe I wouldn't be forever wondering if it's still possible to ever share something like that again.

I can't stop thinking about how sweet it felt, *how wholesome, how pure*, to be surrounded by a handful of souls that knew mine almost as deeply as I did. And it might be the most painful thing in the world, to one day be a friend and a villain of her own doing the next. To braid each other's hair and share sips from the same smuggled bottle of white moscato and convince each other that ice cream in blizzard weather is a *perfect* idea. To fill a whole living room with witchlike cackling and Broadway references and videos of us singing we can't recall the next morning. I miss them almost as much as I miss all of the parts of me they knew.

It's hard unlearning the patterns of who we were when we were happy together, recalibrating the brain to remember how to function in absence. Those nights are still alive in a world where the bonds that once held them together are now breathless.

I drink my tea at the same time every night. I think while I do it—of the things I have and have lost. Theirs are still the names that come to mind first. I think of that night and the countless others. The farmers market on my birthday with the cinnamon jam we didn't buy, the records we flipped through, *The Lumineers* on the ride home. I think of haunting the aisles of the grocery store and home football games where we'd lose our voices before Enter Sandman. I don't want to graduate without making things right. Or at least trying, however fruitless the end result.

It's distressing just thinking about the people we'll be in one year's time. What city will have stolen my heart by next May? What impulsive and likely regrettable decision will I have made with my hair? Will I know the newer versions of them?

Or will I never get the chance to?

I wonder if they wonder.

Where Do Poems Come From?

I can't speak for yours,

but mine—

they fall from the apple trees of memory:

[lunchbox love letters my mother would pack
under kindergarten grilled cheese sandwiches]

[certain smells, like fresh oregano and Old Spice
deodorant and the last day of summer in Virginia]

[the curvature of my first love's cheek, too familiar]

[my heart glowing under tender peacoat buttons
all winter, as if I had swallowed a lamp for you]

[the worst pain I've ever felt]

Oh,

how they thud against unforgiving earth,

while I bend down to juice what is left

of each bruised

[and beautiful]

little world.

Forever After

Pathetically depleted, I wallow in my flesh and dream

of a particular kind of freedom. The painless, childish

sort, like when you're seven and your whole life orbits

around the geometric dome at your elementary school

playground and trading juice boxes for scented erasers.

Holding twenty years in your hands is a great ordeal,

heavier than expected, unlike the gala apples you'd pack

for field trips and forget in the tall grass for picnic ants

to call their own. At seven you don't think much about

pain or the body or what is written in the stars for you.

You just know you like to run, and then you skin your

knee and train yourself to avoid that particular sidewalk

crack forever after, and the only stars you care about

are the ones that twinkle extra hard on your birthday,

and the ones on movie screens, and the ones in your eyes

when you think about how wild and limitless the world

is, the entire sphere inhaling and exhaling just for you.

Eighth Grade

When we weren't looking we grew up—and out
of homecoming parades and school bus field trips
and first-ever crushes, penning *I like you* on loose
leaf paper to slip into the vents of our steel lockers.
If you asked me to the dance, just know I'd say yes.

Curling iron years, learning how to seem cool
and aloof over text, hurling our phones across
the room at sleepovers, masking racing hearts,
Shirley Temples in disposable cups. We were
anything but cool and aloof. I memorized,
with a serial killer's talent, the scent of his
laundry detergent as he passed me before
the homeroom bell. I wanted him forever.

One day I'll marry him, I remember thinking,
over-lining my eyes with sparkling turquoise.
He never asked me to the dance, but I found
I hardly cared. The school cafeteria erupted
in blue light, DJ mixing *Billboard*'s Top 100,
the first week of June 2014, and I danced until
I had to kick off my kitten heels and after that
danced some more. I held my best friend's hand
through the slow songs. I remember how we lost
our voices shrieking the cheesy lyrics, shutting
our eyes and not looking and growing up.

Things That Can Still Make Me Smile

Videos of golden retrievers gentle enough to hold raw eggs between their jaws without biting down, remembering that, to every tiny baby on the planet, the whole world is made of soft voices and spinning mobiles and glow-in-the-dark stars pasted to nursery ceilings. Teary-eyed phone calls from far, far away because at least, in spite of everything, we still have this—*You hang up first!* No, I did last night. *Okay, fine.* The sound of children pedaling training-wheeled bicycles and yelling *On your mark, get set, go!* outside my bedroom window, how sometimes childhood still feels accessible from this vantage point, from the same room I occupied when I was just as wild as them. Ancient footage of the year 2000, when it was soapy baths in the hotel sink and marble-eyed gazing at Barney from my bouncer and dimpled hands reaching for bigger ones. How all of this happened before anything bad ever had the chance to happen, before the days of capital D Diagnosis, before every chapter of hurt and heartbreak, before I spoke the languages of wound and hate. I rewind that gummy smile over and over again, pausing for a moment, wondering if I'll ever think of the world to be as good as it was to me back then. The whole world, so good.

When I Was Nineteen

I left my dorm in knee-deep snow before anyone else woke up. Dug my body into the cold, no destination in mind, just a girl buried in the stillness of morning.

When I was nineteen,

I burned bright red in arms that held me tight. If you were to ask him what it felt like to clutch such a fiery frame, he would have said, "An experience, for sure, but she hurts."

When I was nineteen,

God, I was all about the experience.

When I was nineteen,

I was nineteen and nothing more. Nineteen and everything bold about being awake before everyone else. I was wandering and kissing and breaking and dreaming and fantasizing and planning and shuttling and doing nothing at all.

When I was nineteen,

That was my favorite part. Figuring out how to play with all of that nothingness, that snowy field, those vacant arms, so much everything in nothing. So much me in you.

Ode to 220

Campbell Hall, the first time I met you I cried.
Your paint peeled in layered petals from sticky walls,
crumbling to death. Past midnight after settling in,
I taped photos of my family to your ceiling tiles
as an attempt to make you feel more like *them*,
like *home*, less broken sink and drafty door,
less stuffy air and moldy window sill.

I watched the seasons turn from that top bunk.
Sweaty summer, golden autumn, and then months
and months of endless white. We kept the fans
blowing constantly through knee-deep snow.
If air could be airless, that's what you were:
oppressive and stifling, a prison of heat.
My photos could not stick to your facades.
I watched as they all fell, one by one,
leaves of memory collecting on the concrete floor.

220, you smell of mildew and winter sickness,
of Saturday mornings, someone burning muffins
in the kitchen next door. Of muffled music
playing through cardboard walls, of whispers
that somehow wake the whole world up.
Of no time like the present for being eighteen, then
too quickly nineteen, then suddenly old enough
to finally move on from you. And who knows
how much of me you'll remember, but I think
I've decided to forget you for a while.

It'll be hard, I know,
now that I know so much of you
and you of me. Your walls have numbered
all of my tears, each and every one,
from the moment my parents left for home
and I sobbed through the peephole,
wondering how I would survive the year.

Now it is time to shut you away forever.

I just hope, friend of mine,
that you are as kind to the next one
as you were to me.

Keep her secrets,
her madness, her Scotch-taped photos
and restless midnights. And of course,
(and you'll have no problem
with this one, I'm sure),

Keep her warm through the winter.

Soon spring will come
and she, too, will hesitate at your entrance,
wondering just how to leave you behind,
how to exit the home you have become.

My Last Day as a Child

written the night before my eighteenth birth•ay

is not today.

Even after my roots silver,
bones melted to wax, birthday candles
long since sacrificed for sleep,

I will still be dizzy light and altitude,
propped upon my father's shoulders,
chasing the cobalt shore, fitting my feet
inside his bigger prints.

Still a baby-faced stickler for perfection
wretched eyesight, hunched over
clicking typewriter keys bleeding poetry
from the tips of gentle fingers.

I will still be seventeen and ablaze,
bleaching hair rebellion red,
intoxicated by forehead kisses
on rainy Saturday past-midnights,
safety in split ends and sadness.

Not today.

No abrupt finalities here.

Today is a day for feet crunching
in the shed skin of autumn leaves,

for giggling like a kindergartner
at playground recess that never ends.

My last day as a child will be the last day of my life,
not the eve of my eighteenth revolution around the sun.
She still has enough light to lift me up on tall shoulders,
just as my father did on those windswept sands of time,
receding to oblivion.

Beat on, young heart.
Breathe flame.

You still have far too many lives
left to live. Far too many to claim
forever yours.

II

STORIES BY GHOSTS

Church Street

You'd walk with me to therapy. I'd constantly reassure you that I was capable of getting there alone. After all, the lady was kind. Her office, a couple blocks from campus, was decorated in comforting shades of purple.
She diffused delicious essential oils (usually lemongrass, sometimes lavender), and the entire practice was situated at the top of a pillared mansion,
up the cascading staircase, first door to the right. I knew I'd manage without you. But you didn't care, you knew I secretly preferred it, having a
companion to fool around with before pouring my trauma out on a silver
platter for her to examine and dissect. On the way there, we'd stop for
spicy Chinese noodles, burn our tongues trying to shove it all down
quickly enough to make it to the appointment on time, and then jaywalk
(more like jay*sprint*) across the busy street to beat the idle traffic light.

We were usually alone in the waiting room, watching the sun burn the
telephone wires of our small town the color of a ripe apricot. I'd schedule
my appointments late to avoid the rush hour of other college students
waiting to get their respective brains "fixed." I'd make faces at you from
behind whatever dog-eared, ragged copy of *Good Housekeeping* I could
find, feigning pornographic bedroom eyes just to make you laugh. *You're
a temptress,* you'd say half-jokingly. But that's exactly what I was doing,
tempting you to need me.

My therapist had a name for you: *your friend in the waiting room.* She'd
pop her head out to call my name and wave to you, knowing you'd be
there, one leg coolly folded on your knee, working on homework balanced like a trapeze artist. Inside the room with the door shut, I'd bom-
bard her with the usual pain: my characteristic loss of friends (inevitable,
and always my fault), my abandonment issues, and my unforgiving hos-

tility toward my family for cursing me with the genetics that made me want to kill myself. She'd listen and offer empathy. One night, after our session ended, I had one hand on the doorknob before she stopped me. *Is that sweet boy in the waiting room your boyfriend?* I wanted to say, *He used to be.* I wanted to say, *Kind of.* But instead I said, *No, he's just my friend,* which wasn't a lie, but wasn't a full truth either. *Well,* she replied with a scarecrow-like smile pasted on her face, *You're lucky to have someone like him.*

And I was.

I break out in cold sweat thinking about walking to see her again. I've been putting it off, cancelling appointments, faking soundness of mind just to avoid walking past our token Chinese restaurant with the sticky booths and the chain of mom-and-pop stores perfect for mindless window shopping and the pedestrian light that never turns and Church Street—fittingly named for the Baptist, Presbyterian, Episcopal, Methodist, and Lutheran churches standing stoically one after another like dominoes—where we'd test the door handles of each building hoping one would let us in. It was stupid fun. But you've grown tired of me, and you despise me now, which just means that no one's gonna walk me there if I ever muster enough courage to walk back. No one's gonna sit for a full hour in the waiting room just to take the transit bus with me after sunset so I wouldn't have to ride alone. No one's gonna ask me how it went—*Did you tell her about your parents? How do you feel?*—or squeeze my hand in the dark when it went terribly, the nights I'd dive a little too deeply into my hurt. You were my friend. You held my hand. I didn't know it then, but I needed you.

She'll ask me, *Where's your friend?* And I'll shrug my head and say something like *Not here,* or *Probably just busy,* because I'll talk about anything to anyone—my twisted history, my constant suffering, my wounds that won't heal—but I won't talk about Church Street, or how all of the church doors were bolted shut, or how I wanted to kiss you on the way back, like old times, but didn't.

Holy Whatevers

Chipped coffee mugs half-filled with cheap liquor,
makeshift blanket forts, a locked door. Lipstick
rubs off when I scrub my lips in the shower
but guilt does not; it sits like a sore and festers.
I started to believe in the permanence of those
holy whatevers: paresthetic leg under the weight
of you, static electricity, the pins and needles
of knowing someone almost fully. I say almost
because we never really do. No matter how
easy it becomes to sacrifice sanity, how natural
it becomes to wear each other's smiles like
sweatshirts in a too-hot September, there is more
to a person than who they were when they left.
I thought you were composed of magic, under your
skin a gleam of nirvana; if anyone asked me I could
have sworn you were a god in another hourglass.
Those sacred trivialities: strands of my hair
on your perfumed pillowcase, arguments about
the universe under halcyon skies, a litany
of touching and colliding. The whole world
would call us blasphemy, would deem us sinful.

But I kept my toothbrush in your medicine
cabinet. I kicked your leg in my nightmares.

When you pick your lip, does it still bleed?

Acts of Beautiful Violence

It was your thumb in my mouth, nail scraping roof,
then rivulets of blood collecting in the cracks of my lip.

I liked being bad for you more than I liked being good.
I mean, I liked holding your hand, too, but there was

something deliciously appealing in pinning them down,
anticipating your surrender. As I held you in captivity

certain words came flooding into my consciousness:
religion, August, limitless, distance. And now, years

later, I am still trying to find the poem that exists
within the gaps of those disconnected units, within

fading memories of drying blood on bedsheets, acts
of beautiful violence, the summer we learned to speak.

_____ or Current Resident

Chinese Kitchen on N. Main has been alive
longer than I have. *26th Anniversary, 15% off*
boasts curly lettering, origin Microsoft Word.
I am stunned by the permanence of things.
Last winter an old friend of mine used to peer
into the misty shop window with me, watching
locals passionately devour steamed dumplings.
We swore we'd try them one day but never
got around to it. Dear Current Resident of
Apartment E, take this booklet of coupons,
for *Big Easy Savings, Price◦ Low Every Day.*
If only they knew I wish I could buy time.
That I wish I could fill my plate with heaps
of minutes, that I wish we could have been
permanent enough to make it inside. Maybe
we would've loved their sesame chicken, or
maybe we'd come back over and over for
the house special, or the beef lo mein or
maybe we'd deem it *whatever* and never
come back, passing the open sign every night
but at least we'd know. I've got a phantom
limb taste in my mouth that wouldn't be
there if he had just kept walking me home.

Polychromasia

The pallor of your skin—
speckled eggshell, loose baby teeth,
as white as the lies you'd leave on my lips.
Soaked in moonlight, you appeared to me
an unreal specter though I bathed delicately
in your heat, night after night. A strange thing
it is, to be desperate and drowning in the ivory
of someone else's desire. I wanted to paint you
with my color, to douse the sharp contours
of your skeleton with scandalous pigment,
to make you a canvas for my fire.
And so I clothed you in fingerprints
with the intention of staining you gold
until I found myself standing alone,
palms still dripping with bleach.

A Voicemail

Hey Michelle, so um, I'm in the line for the brownie sun•ae right now, an• um, [emphatically] *they have birth•ay cake ice cream! So I mean, •o we want birth-•ay cake ice cream, or like, •o we still want the espresso chip, like, what's going on here? So yeah, birth•ay cake ice cream, uh, is that a no-go or is that a full-on go, is that a full-sen•?* Uh, let me know. [long pause] *Also si•e note, I love you a lot. Thanks for everything.*

One year, one month, and twenty-nine days (or, if you round up, two months—effective just two hours from now). That's how long it's been since you called me from inside the campus ice cream shop while I sat outside at our usual table, the one tucked in the hidden corner under the veranda. That night, I had lovingly forced you to order for two distinct reasons. First: because, at the time, I had crippling social anxiety that would've undoubtedly sent me hyperventilating in front of the delectable selection of various sorbets and custards, and believe me, that's embarrassing for a nineteen-year-old college student, obviously. Second: because the sky looked particularly holy, so holy that I would've been delighted to die underneath it. Full moon, twinkling ether, accompanied by the chime of shrieking laughter from passersby. I was happier waiting. Besides, our meetings were secret. Hence why we had to camouflage.

So I ignored your call. I figured it wasn't important, and your stupid grin through the glass was confirmation. You shrugged your shoulders in your usual fashion and that was the end of it. Minutes later, you came strolling out, two scoops of espresso chip brownie sundae dripping through the cracks in the cheap paper boat. Melted chocolate seeped through the hollow spaces between your fingers and I remember ugly-laughing at the sight of your foolishness. Typical. *You're a •ork,* I remarked, *I hate it,* and we annihilated our dessert like it was the Last Supper or a final meal before a gruesome electric chair execution.

For over a year now, that voicemail has been buried under twenty or so messages left by eager telemarketers hungry for identity theft and respectfully ignored by yours truly. Today I stumbled upon it, still unread, and decided to click play—only because it had your name on it and I wanted to remember what you sounded like before you swiftly decided you'd never leave another one. I played it. I choked back a burning lump of regret, the furthest thing from sugar-sweet.

What if I knew birthday cake was an option? Would I have chosen it, or would I have stood firm in our silly tradition of *always espresso chip*, flirtatiously calling you a traitor for posing such a blasphemous suggestion? Would I have said *I love you* back? Would I have meant it? Or would I just keep doing that thing I always did with you, apprehensively looking over my shoulder to see if anyone had noticed us? Would I have allowed myself to love you without shame?

It wasn't about birthday cake or espresso chip or even the stars that night. It was, instead, only about—

Also si♦e note, I love you a lot. Thanks for everything.

Also si♦e note, I love you a lot. Thanks for everything.

Also si♦e note, I love you a lot. Thanks for everything.

For what? For letting my phone ring that night, pressing *Reject* because it couldn't have been important enough? For laughing when someone would ask about us, playing dumb and protecting my reputation without regard for how you'd take it?

I play it over and over, the voicemail and the memory of what happened under last year's April stars,

loving you but looking over my shoulder.

Scenic Views from Rock Bottom

You know, I always thought I was a good kisser
until I found myself kissing you, running all the red lights
until you stop me midbreath. Highway patrol, you are.
Slow ɩown. You pull me back to earth.
It's such a casual thing, how you yank me from the moon.

You kiss funny, you say, looking up at me,
all hazy, flushed in the amber light.

I've never been here before.
I don't really speak the same language as you.

To you I am just another numbered voice
tangled in midnight. I am somewhere else,
an astronaut of my own imagination, perhaps
adrift in a backwards world.

What does that mean, I wonder, that I kiss *funny?*
I wonder if my confusion has a taste.

The flavor of my otherness, my cold alien lack of knowledge
about how these things: these brutal, violent,
heartbreaking *things,* work. You kiss me hard
and all I taste is the bitterness of something dying.

This is the death of romance, I think,
falling asleep in your bed. I can't sleep, though,

so does it even count as sleep? I don't know.
I do know that you don't love me.

All of this madness is supposed to mean nothing,
the way it is, most of the time,
in places I've never been until now.

You roll over when it is done
and I watch your expression as you sleep,
connecting the freckles on your chin like stupid,
cursed constellations that feel like they are there
but aren't. I wipe my eyes to forget this art.

Look, I whisper, when morning comes
and the sunrise through your window
paints the buildings of our world pale yellow.

You don't look, though, and that's okay.
You sleep through the gold.

I know I am the only one who can see these things,
sometimes. It's *my* world, after all.

I Was Never Peaceful

She makes you tea. Chamomile.
Water first, then leaves. Let steep.
It's the way you've always taken it, the way
I learned from you—water always cardinal.
And then, while heat emancipates itself, she sits
in your lap and blathers philosophy. The origin
of language and ethics and dreams. It's carnal to you.
Enticing. Intellectual lust has always been a weakness.
You are charmed by girls with vagabond minds, at least
you were for me. Or maybe she does it all backwards.
Leaves first, then water. Opposite arrangements.
And maybe she talks about nothing, just rests
her head on your shoulder and waits in perfect peace.
I was never peaceful. I was bold and combustible
and aggravating, I bet. But you adored it.
That I was violently obsessed with
thinking. Sensually aware—
the god of memorizing
your arrangements
and speaking them.

Unfinished Short Stories

Twilight at the tennis court, heartbeats stuck in the mesh,
this is how I want to remember you. In exaggerated grunts
and lilting laughter, in this scattering half-light you move
like an oil painting finished just moments ago. We're clowns,
both of us, exaggerating our grunts like the pros on TV do.
I run like a fool, serve you the ball, sprint to return it, sky
darkening until we can't make out the white lines anymore.

This is how I want to remember you, along with the other
vignettes I carousel between in my head. Like origami cranes
hung from loft bed frames, too much cologne, a single red
rose. My hair stuck in your window fans, turtlenecks in July
because you could never help yourself, how we concealed
our contrabands: boxed chardonnay, what happened behind
the parked tractor, the secrets we'd swap. That one time we
went to that psychedelic poetry exhibit with the rotating
walls that made us hallucinate for hours, how afterward
we lay flat on our backs to trace fake constellations with
our pointer fingers, how we'd always walk home stained
by grass and drunk on the absurd philosophies we'd invent.

This is how I want to remember you, in these short stories
only you know the endings to, but mostly that one night,
at the tennis court, when we were clowns and the lines were
there, fencing us in, holding us close, until they couldn't.

Great Danes and Tea Bags

I like to imagine you reading my poetry. It's almost sadistic, how desperately I wish to witness your pupils nervously flitting from line to line, configuring words into something resembling *meaning*, occasionally stumbling upon a memory of ours and swallowing hard. I play the reverie over and over in my mind. A blink. A clearing of the throat, then an Adam's apple following shortly behind. Yes, I'm a little sick in the head.

I like to imagine that the act of doing so is something secret, privately profane, only permissible once she falls asleep so there are no questions asked that you can't answer. Like why you care so much about what I have to say, or why you have to wait until two in the morning to tediously unravel what I've made. I like to imagine you killing time until her eyelids flutter shut before finally letting the glow of your screen suffuse your skin. And then you begin, catching glimpses of your face in every "you" I've written.

The images come in brutal flashes. There we are in June, in my car, the wind blowing so ruthlessly I keep choking on my own hair. It's our seventeenth summer. I'm learning how to drive and I hit every curb. You're smoking the cigarettes you stole from your older brother which he stole from your dad. You're laughing at me. You can't look away.

Tonight, you can't look away, either. You sink silently into each aching recollection. That time we almost adopted the Great Dane we didn't have one square foot of space for. How you'd tie tea bag strings around my ring finger, promising me the whole world.

In the morning she'll kiss you awake and ask how you slept. And you'll say *It was fine.* But you won't mention how stealthily you had to cry, careful not to disturb her peace.

To Tell You the Truth

I was banking on forever.

Carving pumpkins with you the day after Halloween,
pulps already rotting, you'd stick your slender fingers
into that cavernous decay and laugh like a serial killer.

I secretly loved it, watching your jack-o'-lantern smile
flicker through slime-covered hands. Stupid kid, you.
Sometimes I loved you so much I wanted to hurt you.

I know I did in the end.

Do you remember our belated Halloweens as vividly
as I do? And our makeshift birthday parties, just us
and two slices of store-bought wedding cake rejects.
Our Christmases, even though you couldn't grasp
the concept of Jesus and hated commercialization,
how we'd unwrap each other's gifts and feign surprise.
I liked to trick myself into thinking you knew me less
than you actually did. How it kept the mystery alive,
kept you intrigued enough to keep undoing me, but

to tell you the truth

I was banking on forever.

I still don't know how to *Halloween*
or *holi•ay* or *preten• that I •on't wish
I still •i•*. It's almost October and if

someone were to peer through my skin,
they'd find that nothing glows, no light,
just a faint flicker if you trick yourself
long enough to believe in ghost stories.

.

A Dare

Cut the pretense. I mean, really chop it off. Sever the fist you form. Let the blood flow; see how it stains every word you write.

What I mean is I want to write a poem about something real. These days I'm starved for it, all of that pulsing realness. I want to feel a poem breathe into my mouth. I crave it even in my sleep, something raw and gritty caressing my unconscious face. I want to be woken up by reality even if it means drenching my sheets in cold sweat. I'd even be thankful to die like that.

I want to write about suffering—not as metaphor, not as forced comparison or abstract expression. I want to write about suffering like the fact of the matter is that last night I fell asleep praying for snow but this morning's clouds simply could not deliver. We woke up to dry sidewalks and heavy skies. I want to write about how snow makes me think of you, but not in some sort of romantic gesture, mostly just you, in all of your realness, those days we were stranded indoors. We woke up to endless white; I woke up to you kissing me alive again. I want to write a poem about perfect suffering. I feel like it would read something like walking with you, months later, wanting to melt the flurries on your cheeks with my own. All this and I cannot touch you. That's how you write suffering. I wanted to touch you but I know I'd melt more than just snow.

This is me cutting the pretense. This is me choosing to melt us anyway. This is me reaching out to touch you in a way I can only do with words. This is me staining the paper. This is me flowing back to you, the realest poem I've ever bled.

It Was Never About Tea

Ballpoint poems on chewing gum wrappers,
my words a brisk mint dancing on your tongue.
I'd slip them inside your notebooks to unfold
on harder days, writing you into a new world
when your real one would crumble. We used
to make tea and then forget to drink it. Now
I realize it was not forgetfulness, but our own
vernacular. There, in the cooling steam, was
our way of sharing understanding, letting
each other steep in these invented routines.
Effortless vocabulary: flushed faces, sudden
downpours, blurry snapshots of hip bones
painted by morning light, no need to speak.
Superficial nothings, trifles that glimmer;
when the patterns finally broke so did I.

Though We Were Anything but Holy

You don't believe in God, only an indifferent universe. I know this because, one night, under invisible stars, I asked you what you thought happened to our souls when we die. And you told me souls were merely constructs invented by humans as a way to keep pretending our lives possess any real importance. I told you that was stupid before you could keep philosophizing, tearing apart every possible creation myth like the Devil's most infuriating advocate. Picture it now: a self-righteous atheist lying next to a girl raised on Sunday school and plastic rosary beads. Textbook polar opposites, flip sides of coins, conflicts of interest. I fell in love with you because you were everything I could not stand.

When you went backpacking across crowded tourist spots in foreign cities I could hardly pronounce, you flooded my phone with photos from the insides of grand cathedrals. Stained glass windows, gold crucifixes, gothic architecture so dramatic it could make nonbelievers believe in *something.* I never asked for those pictures, not even one, but you sent them anyway, perhaps knowing subconsciously that I would feel something sacred stirring inside of me. From behind the lens, you were not contemplating the shape of God, but the shape of my wonder upon receiving what you could capture.

You, standing awestruck by martyrs carved from ancient wood. You, a skeptic, rejecting all notions of a life apart from this one. You, contemplating the illusion of heaven, and somehow thinking only of me.

I'm not sure what or Whom I believe in anymore, apart from the gallery of images I can't bring myself to delete. I flip through them one-by-one, imagining your gaze finding something beautiful enough to steal, for a moment, and send across the ocean to a wholehearted believer shifting quietly in her sleep.

Textbook polar opposites, flip sides of coins, conflicts of interest. I fought you in the twin bed we shared until I went red in the face and cried at my lack of ability to change your mind. I fought you on a park bench in January during that record-breaking blizzard until our shoulders were covered in pearly white. I fought you in front of our old friends after you brought up your stupid politics and conspiracy theories and when you looked at me and said *Facts don't care about your feelings* and actually meant it.

But back when it was simple, you were just an atheist in a cathedral praising God without meaning to.

You thought of me. You sent me photos. You were an icon of irony.

To remember it now, though we were anything but holy.

That once, I believed in God and you, in me.

Persimmons Under Evergreen Trees

The story continues elsewhere— somewhere
no longer habitable—in a secret place
beyond the fringes of bodily reach. I know this to be true
because I can still feel the physical movement
of anatomies ripe with call and response,
weight shifting and unfolding like origami paper,
hidden flesh creasing then collapsing.

The story—*our* story—endures
in the memory of its telling.

In that secret place we are still allowed
to share persimmons under evergreen trees,
spitting seeds into stiff grass, colliding teeth
with nectarous juice still dripping from our lips.

In that secret place we are still allowed
to wash each other's backs,
treating each vertebrae like gospel, scrubbing
the peaks and valleys of our earthly forms
until we are made new again.

I know that place exists
because sometimes I wake to the taste of winter fruit
as if I'd bitten into something ripe just seconds ago,
or the sensation of fingers skimming the dips of my spine,

a feeling like coming home.

And I know it's you—

reaching out from that other world we cannot visit
where the story never ends—
and that it has to be you,
because no one moves me the same way, or ever could,

in this one.

Subject:

I want to send you an email. Not a postage-stamped handwritten letter, my soul tucked away in a white envelope and licked shut. I can't stand the possibility of you turning the key to your apartment mailbox and finding a piece of me drowned in a tsunami of overdue bills and months-expired coupon books. I'd rather let my words get lost to oblivion in an online in-box. Or better yet, your automatic spam folder, brimming with useless junk and phishing bots. I want you to know so many things without you having to read them, lump in your throat, sick to your stomach. I know I hurt you. I know my apologies are knives that still twist, months later. Would you delete it? I'd understand.

Should I start with *Dear [Re•acte•]* or just *[Re•acte•]* followed by a comma, plain and painless? Does *Dear* leave too much to interpretation, too much "You are *•ear* to my heart, and you still have so much of it in the palm of your hand"? Because that would be embarrassing. Should I begin with vague pleasantries—*I can't believe it's June. I'm •rowning in that Northern Virginia subtropical humi•ity! I know you remember how awful it feels. Anyway, how have you been coping with everything? Wil•, uncertain times.*

Should I dive in headfirst or dip my toes in the water? You make me want to take the plunge, to curse all possible consequences and damn them to the deep. You always have.

The cursor tempts. I want to give in. No repartee, just my heart in all of its nakedness.

Dear [Redacted],

The lack of you unsettles me. Your absence is ear-splitting and all I can do is listen.

Is someone else making you happy? If so, I wonder what her name sounds like spilling off your tongue. Does it cascade like honey? Does she kiss your shoulders like it's the last time, every time? I trust your taste. I just know she's lovely without having to meet her.

What did you do with all of the letters I wrote you? Do they still occupy the bottommost drawer of your computer desk, still secured in that crinkly pink wrapping paper? Or, if you had to get rid of them, did you choose to recycle? That sounds like you. There's comfort in imagining my words being made new, serving some grander purpose. Cleaned and re-processed and reincarnated. I like the idea of that, another chance.

I'm reading more than usual these days. It's a way to kill time and I'm always killing time; it's how I cope. Have you heard of the novel *Normal People* by Sally Rooney? Probably not. It reminds me a lot of us. Weaving in and out of each other's timelines, stopping for a brief moment to sit longingly and absorb as much of each other as humanly possible before having to diverge again. Never a last time with you. Never a last time loving you, either. Too much? Sorry.

I shouldn't be writing you. I have a life that needs tending to. I kiss someone else now and I fully adore him. Please try your hardest to not misunderstand. But I'm going through the motions of this strange design, this exotic geometry, and I can't stop thinking about the second nature easiness of belonging to someone like you. Rummaging through your closet without asking, to find something soft enough to sleep in. Associating *skin* with *holy*—not *sin* or *hell*. Careful back rubs when I would doze off mid-panic attack. Now all you are to me is a fleeting vision I can't touch. Weird, right?

As much as I want you to remember me as a giggling, wavy-haired siren ogling you from across the room (and all of our seemingly endless distances) I know you probably don't. My mind romanticizes the woman I was for you. I could've sworn I did everything right.

But I didn't and no one understands that more than you. You were the target at the end of my barrel. The test drive forever. The dry run lover. The body I gave up on. I know that kept you up at night.

I wonder if your favorite tea is still chai and if you drink it with her and while she sits in your lap and calls you *baby* (does that still make you blush?) Do you still wash your hair in the sink because it's more convenient? Do you still insist on the same brand of underwear and refuse to even try any other kind? That's still the silliest thing to me.

Tell me anything or nothing. It's alright, whichever one you choose.

Remember I'm always here,

M

Part I: Chapter Endings From a Book I'll Never Write

Alternate titles:

A Collection of Real an◦ Fake Stories: All Involving Han◦-Hol◦ing

Represse◦ Trauma, but Make It Art

These Characters Aren't Real, so Stop Guessing

Or Are They? Perhaps Partially

Even in the dim of the theater, I was almost *too* aware of him. I can't precisely describe the awareness, but it was as if the act of him sitting next to me made his presence an extension of my body. Our hands did that stupid thing you see in coming-of-age movies: dangling off the sticky arm rests, clammy palms "accidentally" grazing, every tiny shift electric-shocking up my arm. And the next thing you know, he's holding my hand. It just happens. It feels like dying a thousand oxytocin-fueled deaths, like that *Sublime* shit you hunt for in English literature. He fingers the dips between my knuckles and I, glowing scarlet, turn to him in that pale cinema light and tease by whispering *I'm not your fucking piano*. We do that throughout the whole movie. I don't even remember how it ends; that's how overwhelmed I was by his knee weighing against mine, the nectarous smell of him so new and already saturating my lungs. When I got home, I paced my room trying to catch my breath for an hour. I couldn't shower. I just kept looking at the ticket stub, a madwoman unsteady and aching to time travel back to just hours before when I hadn't yet felt the rush of him close to me. I wanted to experience that completely submerged, utterly inundated sinking feeling for the first time again. I still can't cough it out of my lungs.

Part II: Chapter Endings From a Book I'll Never Write

Compromised by five different varieties of sketchy juice, S* asked me with bambi eyes if I'd ever, in the history of our knowingness, had "real feelings" for him. Almost too enthusiastically, I said *yes* because how could I not? My feelings were always real, especially with him; in retrospect he should've known that. Thin frame painted by the glowing lamp posts outside, he ran his fingers down my arm and professed I had the smoothest skin he'd ever touched and then only after the goosebumps formed did he tell me I kissed funny and I lost sleep over that for months, even when I started kissing other people. In the morning our eyelids fluttered open and he put on *The E●ge of Seventeen* and I felt seventeen, the kind of seventeen I never got to live. I clutched his hand and he did mine and I thought he was into me, that to him I was as sound as gospel. But he dropped me off after sunrise, hurriedly mumbled something along the lines of *see ya aroun●* and left me pondering, yearning for days. The next day, a text: *I have your necklace. It's on my nightstan●.* I told no one about it.

But I didn't care about the necklace. I wished I could've left more of me behind. I wished he had loved me, even just for a little bit, an afternoon or an evening or even just in a sentence. For a few hours I felt like his stereotypical indie film girlfriend, the one who'd write poetry about his dark eyes and dark hair and how he wasn't my type but that didn't matter, especially with him; I could be his manic pixie dream girl for good. To him I meant fling, to me he meant forever. I imagined meeting his mom, sitting on his family couch, resting my head on his dog's stomach, flipping through the plastic album sleeves of his baby books. Who does that after a casual affair? I can't watch *The E•ge of Seventeen* anymore. I can't think about that window view, or of "real feelings" and all of the light waking up and me silently begging *stay, stay asleep just a little while longer, •on't walk me home, not now, not yet, not ever.*

*S: redacted. His name doesn't even start with an S. He might not even be real. Stop guessing.

Part III: Chapter Endings From a Book I'll Never Write

Alternate titles:

A Collection of Real an♦ Fake Stories: All Involving Han♦-Hol♦ing

Represse♦ Trauma, but Make It Art

These Characters Aren't Real, so Stop Guessing

Or Are They? Perhaps Partially

On his nightstand: fifteen orange pill bottles lined up like plastic soldiers ready for war, a marble guitar pick nearly bent in half, an empty dream journal, and above it all, a gaping hole in the drywall from the night I told him all of it was too much for me. I hated holding his hand. It felt like clutching something clinging to life by a thinning thread, a run-over animal laboring for its last breaths. "Come closer," he'd say, but closer was everywhere I couldn't stand to be. His room reeked of grief, of months-unwashed sheets and sour sickness and my foolish inability to relate. His pain was fragrant and all I could do was soak in it, graceless. He only praised my poetry when it bled. I think this was his way of entertaining a pent-up fantasy of us taking over the world, one miserable line at a time. I never kissed him, not even on his good days. I was too afraid that, by loving him even slightly, I'd kill him. But I think that's what I did anyway, albeit in a different way, killed him so good he ended up writing seven awful songs with my first name plastered right there in the titles. I listened to them secretly, hearing him curse me under dissonant guitar chords, those bedroom lullabies damning me to hell. For months I wondered why. Was it because I couldn't stomach the portrait of him: unkempt, rageful, defeated? That I couldn't mask my discomfort under the ballads I'd write for him? That I never knew what to say when he wept over his own survival? And then I remembered. I had penned a letter: *I can't love you the way you want me to.* It was only after I arrived home, after slipping it into his unzipped backpack, that I realized. It was his birthday.

Every Time I See Someone Who Walks Like You

I hold my breath. From across the empty soccer field
by our apartment complex on Wednesday afternoon
I could have sworn I saw the exact outlines of a body
I used to memorize by heart—slender-legged, poor
posture, meandering through the chemically treated
grass with no sense of direction. You used to pace
the forest *just thinking. About what?* I'd ask you,
after you'd disappear for hours without warning.
Nothing really, you'd say, and shrug your shoulders
far too casually for me to believe. But those nights,
playing with your pale blond baby hairs and forcing
you to guess the words I'd write sloppily on your back
with my fingertips (*the answer was always I love you*)
I didn't feel the need to know what you were thinking.
It's funny how *Nothing really* suffices until it doesn't.
Until I'm squinting my eyes from a hundred feet away,
wondering if the dimensions of the wandering man
match yours. But the mathematics are always a little
bit skewed. He's either too tall or not tall enough,
sporting an outfit you'd never wear. *Tell me, •o you
ever try to fin• me in the sha•ows of other people?
Do you hol• your breath until you're wrong, too?*

Rhapsody in Remember Whens

I am sick of writing about you
in *remember whens* or even really at all.

But I remember when I'd watch you brush your teeth
in the fogged-up mirror, humming in perfect pitch
to whatever new indie album we happened to be playing
through your shitty plastic speaker that kept cutting out
and how I'd come from behind to tickle your sides,
making you spit blue foam all over the running faucet.
You hated when I did that and I remember when
pissing you off was my favorite hobby, leaving the light on
after we'd crawl into bed, mocking the way you'd pronounce
certain words like how you made "tour" rhyme with "sewer"
instead of "pour" and how I'd always tell you that everything you did
was wrong. How you'd tie your shoes like an overgrown preschooler,
forming perfect bunny ears, or how you'd never think to double-check
the weather forecast until we were both dripping with summer sky,
clothes drenched and bodies shivering. I am sick of thinking
about any of this, or about how I bruised your forearm
when I got mad enough to kill you, how I came crawling back
before you had the chance to heal. Sometimes I remember
when I did everything I could've possibly done to make you hate me—
piling my dirty dishes in your kitchen sink, rejecting your calls,
trash-talking your friends out of jealousy that anyone other than me
could be allowed the sacred privilege of loving you—
until you gave up and finally did.
Remember when you ⋅i⋅n't?

The Part I Leave Out

Before you left me in the freezing rain, you offered me your jacket. That's the part I always leave out when I tell that story, that you cared even as you broke me. I said *No, it's alright, I'm going inside soon anyway.* But I couldn't. I walked until the January sky birthed amber light again. I bought two scoops of apple pie custard from the corner shop we frequented in the summer and observed the typical crowd of Friday night partygoers stumbling through the streets, buzzing with electric commotion in oversized parkas. I felt something drip through my fingers. I realized I hadn't had a single bite.

I decided to teach myself how to hate you. I sat under the sycamore after twilight and pressed rewind on our story, projecting it in technicolor on the backs of my eyelids. *Reinvent it,* I told myself. *Write a new story.* And just like that, you became the villain.

When they started asking where you went, I told them *He just got tired of hurting me.*

When they asked if I had ever loved you for real, I responded with *How could I?*

But how could I not?

What I still haven't told them is that you introduced me to apple pie custard and people-watching and the shade of the biggest sycamore in town. That you brought me French cinema and paperback books containing images of every known species of butterfly and that yes, I loved you for real, so real that even when you had nothing left to offer but the warmth of your jacket, I knew even at that moment that I could never stop.

Between Feral Fingers

I want to go home and I do not mean
where I grew up, the townhouse with
the peeling red shutters and ten goldfish
preserved in alcohol and buried in the backyard.
When I say I want to go home I mean the bend
of your neck in November and semi-golden strands
slipping like silk between feral fingers and
limitless anatomy and not enough time to take
all of it in. I associate home with haunting
bookshelves at the library, peering between
uneven stacks of alphabetized encyclopedias
and then walking home and kicking off
our shoes without untying them first.
Home is desperate—all of our hasty acts,
the sacred profane, leaving nothing unsaid
and no parts untouched. I want nothing
more than to go there, to stop for a while
and observe our geography—three summers
and lifetimes of passion—to visit long enough
to absorb it all for good. Would you let me climb
into your bed, pull the covers over my head?
Or would it be too much, too real to relive?

Tell me before I try.

Main Street

There are over 10,000 Main Streets in the United States of America. They're scattered everywhere. Focal points of Christmas card townships, city corners, college campuses. You can envision a Main Street in your mind without even needing to visit one: strings of charming gift shops, a historic post office, probably a dilapidated dry cleaning service or two with boarded up windows. I must confess, I am pathetically in love with the self-righteous importance of Main Streets. They're not just *streets*, but capital M *Main Street*s. Every local knows which street you're talking about. *The only one that really matters aroun* here.

I can't walk down the Main Street we knew anymore because that's just something that happens when you love someone and they leave. You start taking the long way home, even when the sun sets and you'd theoretically be much safer as a woman walking under Main Street's lampposts rather than traversing the unlit, soulless alleyways. You start driving past Main Street without letting your eyes flit left or right, because you know that you'll see them—*them*— those young, red-faced couples standing at the corner, waiting for the pedestrian light to turn. If I look a little too long, the girl in the red coat becomes me. She's wiping the fog from the boy's clear-rimmed glasses with her scarf like I did for you.

Maybe one day I'll be brave enough to stand at that light alone until it turns. Maybe I'll walk to the coffee shop where we used to order spicy chai in late October and watch the hungover college kids meander through the farmers market, toting around loaves of sourdough bread and orange wildflowers through unrelenting nausea. I'll have no one to laugh at them with but the tea would be just as sweet. I'll just have to make it work.

There are over 10,000 Main Streets in the United States of America but *only one that matters* to me. It's the one nestled in the heart of Southwest Virginia, where we'd peer into the high-end clothing stores and pretend we could afford the outfits on the window mannequins. It's the one where we snuck into that record store and I went home with miscellaneous 60s, Bonnie Tyler, *Jesus Christ Superstar,* and Vivaldi's *The Four Seasons.* That was the day we ran to the bus stop in the rain, your socks drenched and hair glued to your forehead and I knew it. *I coul• never love anyone like this again.*

On Main Street I watched your eyes fill with rain as you sang *Happy Birth-•ay* to me over chocolate cheesecake. On Main Street we shared blood orange sorbet on the bench and watched the usual crowd of night revelers stumble into bars. On Main Street we joked about being married college professors like the ones we'd spot at the underrated sushi place. On Main Street we thought it would all work out.

Maybe one day I'll stop taking the long way home.

Closer Than Flesh

You're tethered to every part of me,
invisible umbilical cord. I can't get rid of you.
I brush my teeth at noon and you're there, too—
laughing through toothpaste foam and hogging the sink
like it's all yours, only yours. I trudge home under the glow
of our flickering street lights and remember arguing with you
about something you'd said earlier that I misinterpreted,
took your joke as a knife in the side rather than what
it really was—an attempt to carry some color to my face.
You're a phantom limb. You're the other end
of the rope and I'm the pathetic tug-of-war loser.
I rest under our tree sometimes and am transported
backwards, to the midnight I first touched you.
You're flushed and you're timid and you paint me
like an artist. A cheek, then a collarbone,
then suddenly you're closer than flesh
and I'm all yours, only yours.

Mahogany

Insulated water bottles filled to the brim with illicit spirits, our bare backs pressed flat against the secret slopes of Appalachia. Tipsy fingers meddled with the buttons on my cardigan until we found it in the sweet grass hours later, soaked in starlight and the dewy scent of us. We were the architects of makeshift movie theaters on your bedroom floor, pirating campy '80s films yet always giving up halfway through with lips trapped between teeth. You'd knead the stubborn knots from the small of my back and I'd thank you afterward with cloudy stories of my past exhaled into your ear. You cried with me. You walked with me through every sunlit garden, stopping me by the conifers to capture the way the dying day would paint my skin mahogany. You were always ready with your camera, waiting for my face to melt for you, how I'd come at you with *No, I don't look good today,* how you'd look at me in breathless disbelief and call me blind. Go on and give the world to someone else. Fill the bottles again. Find new hills for twinkling nights. Sit through the credits this time. Clutch her closer than skin when she shatters. And take pictures of her, too, under any sliver of golden light you can find. She might hate it then but she'll love it later. I know I do. I still look back at those photos and ache that I couldn't believe you.

Eighth Wonder of the Apartment Kitchen

I keep thinking about the time I tried to convince you that substituting olive oil for the vegetable oil I had forgotten to toss into my grocery cart earlier that day would work perfectly fine for the recipe. *It's just oil,* I shrugged. *An• ginger snaps are spicy enough to mask the •ifference, anyway.* Leaning over the kitchen counter, slumped in your usual posture, you shook your head omnisciently and promised me it wouldn't. *Just trust me,* you said. But I've always been stubborn—especially with you—so I ignored your rash foreshadowing and poured the pale green liquid until it spilled over the edge of the measuring cup. Into the batter it settled. You smiled as I relished in my own genius, twirling in circles, a kitchen fairy.

When the oven beeped, our cookies had turned dog shit beige and lumpy. The texture and flavor reeked of my poor judgment. As I disgustedly dumped the contents of the tray into the disposal, I remember taking note of the depth of your stare—half pure fascination, half all-knowing. You were certain I wouldn't listen; I hardly ever did. You just wanted to observe me, annoyingly persistent and forever set in my ways. In your eyes I was the Eighth Wonder of the Apartment Kitchen.

I should've heeded your advice about the oil. And then again, when you warned me through sticky tears that the man I would eventually leave you for would squander me like a counterfeit, like a lousy batch. If I were a real genius of foresight, I would've saved the batter for tomorrow. I'd siphon it into Tupperware until I could buy a cheap bottle of the proper oil. We'd just bake tomorrow.

Maybe I'd even stay with you, instead of fleeing from the only person who cared enough to adore me, even in the failure of my own false prophecy.

To be observed like that by another soul again. To be understood and adored—*just trust me*—before the timer went off and it was time to reveal what we had made.

J

That time, late January, when you met me under the elm tree at the corner of our block after midnight. How we walked for miles under cloud-covered stars, bodies mercilessly stiffened by winter, how I cried in the cornfield because the man I loved couldn't love me back at the depth that I could for him. That night, you and I walked to the grocery store, frost-bitten and numb, and I bought a shitty-looking pizza Lunchables to share with you at the empty playground. It was the first thing I had eaten in days. We weren't disappointed because it was *so* comically shitty—what was supposed to be sauce was gelatin shaped into a solid cube—I remember cracking up with you through frozen tears over that. Those days, laughter was a rarity for me. J, I remember your hands being warm. I don't remember how they ended up in mine. How your thumb danced over my knuckles, skipping across the ridges, unsettlingly hot and intoxicatingly familiar. You told me you were my best friend and kissed me on the forehead, even though I knew you wanted worlds more of me than what you got. I knew we both wished we were allowed to touch like that in broad daylight, that I didn't have to keep you clandestine.

I guess I assumed I was keeping you safe by keeping you secret. That we could always take the last bus to nowhere, that you could always trace shapes on my kneecaps, that we could always end up lying on my bed and accidentally touching, over and over again, undercover lovers under my covers.

J, you're a song I can't play. You're a loveless night. I want you to know that my hands are still cold and I still haven't touched anyone half as warm as you.

Dead Rain

Soaked by sudden storm, rain saturating the apples
of our cheeks, there was a time for dripping hair.
You and I, howling while running for shelter.
And after drying each other's shivering figures,
making soup. There was a time for that, too,
warming numb faces against steaming bowls,
letting the blood return, painting us pink again.

But time does not keep
and cannot endure.
It must make room for other downpours,
new bodies to fill its vacancies, fresh forms.

I run with someone else now, and before the sky pours
we're already home. But sometimes,
when there is no water to wring from my clothes
and my hair still looks the way it did when I left
I remember making soup, heat rising calmly
to meet us, all of our leaking laughter—
you and your still-wet smile.

Perfect Incompletions

I lent you

weak-spined paperback books, coins for your bus fare home,
the defenselessness of my body in late September, eager
silhouettes playing against peeling paint and dying light.

You lent me

halves of your sandwiches, chronicles from childhood,
the nape of your neck where I would trace my name
with my lips to make you appear more real
to me, more conscious.

I liked to imagine
shaping you with my palms
like some sort of maniacal artist.
As if you were my pottery, my life's work,
that I could shape you however I saw fit,
keeping you on the wheel
to be governed by my movements.

But the body is not clay
nor soulless.
It cannot spin forever.
It does not defy inertia.

With you I learned
that the body is only lent in intervals

and then taken back after it is due.
I thought I'd have my whole life
to sculpt you without flaw, but you,
my almost magnum opus,
are my holy unfinished.

Pretending That I Don't

I think I love you
in a different language now—
through gritted teeth at the mindless mention
of your name in conversation, a clenched fist
perspiring against the loose seams of my pocket,
a sealed and stamped envelope I *almost* dropped

into the post office mailbox this morning yet
ultimately decided to save for another day
because *why, what's the point anymore*

if you never check your mail or even check on me,
or if you already know my letter will begin with *sorry*

or *remember when we use♦ to* or *I just wish I♦ been better,*

the contents of my heart translated into cursive bullshit.
So I slipped the letter back into the crease of my coat
and let it burn a hole there, like I'd been shot in the side.
Then I wandered around town, stopping at our landmarks,
pretending it didn't throb and that I wasn't spilling out.
It's funny, though, the things I do to keep you alive.
Like how I still sprinkle cinnamon into black coffee
the way you did for me when I'd rage at you, or how I still
take the scenic route when I drive home, even if no one sits
in my passenger seat pointing at the cows grazing on hills
while cranking '80s rock like we're the main characters
in a trashy romantic comedy that flopped in the theaters,
or how I still write you into my poems even when I run
out of words capable of saying what I've been needing to.
I still love you in past tense, in isolation, in pretending

that I don't. But it's alright, and I'm gonna be fine,
because at least I can still hold you close
in the stories that I tell.

If This Is It

Remember me happy. Remember me a giggling wild thing nuzzled into the freckled bend of your elbow. Remember me dancing, mandarin orange peels in both hands, under the soft overhead light of your apartment kitchen. Remember me flailing my arms to our song in your car, embarrassing you silly in front of all the others waiting for the light to turn. Remember me chasing your little cousin in that chalked-over driveway, spawning into a monster of his imagination just to hear his wicked childish laughter fill our air. Remember me so in love with you I could've died right there, having lived a full life with nothing else I could've dreamed of needing. There was no poverty with you.

If this is it, remember me sparkling. Remember me spinning in that dress for you, all satin and magic and woman and alive. Remember me cracking jokes with your brothers at dinner, the first summer I met your parents, that April I first wrote of you, for you. Remember me in memories of my kicked-off boots at your front door, my seventh heaven dive under your covers. Remember me intoxicated by hope. The very first time I kissed your cheek, my nineteenth springtime in full bloom, how the pink rising in your face competed with everything blossoming around us. Remember me richly yours. Remember me happy.

Song of Solomon and of Myself

What is the proper way to say
don't wait for me, *for I have foun*
the one whom my soul loves?
What is the proper way to pledge
allegiance to a new nation, to emigrate
from the history of self, seeking asylum
from the body you once called home?
What is the proper way to beg God
for new skin? For a waist you never traced,
for bones you never bit? Jesus, teach me
how to bleed in reverse, watch the red
pour back into my side, the art
of never being crucified. What is the proper
way to love? Must it always equate
with sacrifice? Is there a way to say *hol* me*
without anticipating the wound, to say *take*
me without feeling the lance go in,
and out, and in again?

Don't wait for me, for
I have foun the one whom my soul loves.*
Teach me love that leaves without a stain.

III

SHAPES OF DEVOTION

Part to Whole

Because what am I if not handwritten letters,
signed, stamped, and sealed—writing tangled
as if perpetually in a rush to find you? And what am I
if not a flustered bundle of nerves and blood and skin,
pouring all of my wreckage into words and white envelopes,
either too deep in love or too busy looking for it,
always on the hunt for another bundle to belong to?
And who would I be if not a poet?
If not a soul nourished by the sun,
by long walks to nowhere, shoelaces caked in mud?
If not fueled by passion, addicted to the way light
falls gently on your shoulders, soaking up the way
you speak to me—lush and lovely in the dying light?
Because who am I, truly,
if not this strange way that I love—
sponge-like, obsessive, untamable
love? It feeds me. It sustains me,
this hungry way of living:
watching you breathe and
needing to capture every color.

Nothing Else

Light plays on the ridges of your collarbones
and I have determined that I love you most
fast asleep, a human prism painted by morning.
This moment, I want to preserve it for the rest of time:
your chest rippling in waves, cresting and crashing
under an overcast Saturday sky, acoustic guitar swelling
from my next-door-neighbor's apartment kitchen radio.
I wonder where sleep takes you. Am I with you, there?
Or are your dreams wild and boyish, full of outgrown
aggression and muddy knees and brutal brotherhood?
Me, I dream of nothing else but this warm light
and how it chisels you, melting your features
into marble, an act of practical worship.
Nothing else but steady breathing,
this morning, faint music.

Déjà Vu

When God finished shaping the earth,
I wonder if His hands, still caked in clay,
trembled at the sight of something so new.

I imagine Him wiping the dew from his brow,
a soft sigh escaping into the starlight.
Nothing will ever be the same again,
He must have thought, as He perfected Man
and left him, sound asleep, to wake in paradise.

And I only wonder this because I, too, tremble
feeling the precious weight of your hand in mine.
Something about the way you squeeze back
when I do reminds me of creation.
Genesis is found in the streaks of your irises,
safe blue, treacherous blue, same blue,
same feeling He must have felt
looking down into His new ocean
and weeping for the first time.

Nothing will ever be the same again,
I thought. And nothing was,

and ever will be, with you.

Portrait of Paradise

To my right, a setting sun, sinking behind the rooftops.
To my left, a sleeping boy, face painted by her colors.

I could wake him and put on a record—
Vivaldi: The Four Seasons, perhaps—

yet I do not. In the spaces of our shared silences breathes
something sacred, something reminiscent of the Garden.
He is bathed in orange, cast in gold, shadowed by clouds,
yet wholly unaware of how desperately I wish I could
stop daylight from vanishing, how tragic this brevity.

These are moments to which words cannot hold a candle.

And music, though I live for melody filling the air,
would only stain and ruin the perfection of *now.*

I do not wake him. I let the vinyls rest.

And I, too, rest, letting the Artist do the work.

The Sun Came Out on the Day of Love

for the first time in weeks. The LED destination signs
flashing from my college's transit buses shouted *Happy
Valentine's Day!* as they picked up and dropped off
baggy-eyed college students from Point A to B. I saw
a cadet in uniform stumble off the platform and nearly
flat on his face, arms filled with handpicked wildflowers.
I almost cried at his grand gesture, that blooming
determination. I forgot how long it had been since
I last felt the warm sun kissing my face in this city.
Weeks, probably. Noticing its tender rays meeting
the apples of my cheeks and feeling as close to heaven
as first love. The sun came out on the day of love
and I felt like a blind man finding the outlines of a life
previously unknown to him. Couples sprawled out
under sturdy oaks in the dead of February. I folded
construction paper down the center, traced half
a shape, and cut along the lines. How perfect this
world feels when we have great loves worth chasing,
celebrating, the timeless stuff that fills the heart,
expanding and contracting, inwards and outwards.
I wish every afternoon could feel like this, sugar cubes
melting on the tongue, chocolate induced tummy
aches, pink lipstick hearts plastered on your skin.

The sun came out on the day of love
and this is all I need to believe in it again.

How Great Thou Art

for our sweet Appalachia

Mornings in the mountains are to the soul as honey is to a sore throat. I swear I could live like this forever: cheeks stained midwinter pink, quick forehead kisses before the light turns green again, your thumb surfing easy across my knuckles during the Our Father. These are the days we bundle up snowman-style over our Sunday best, giggle in coffee breath, warm our faces over something freshly pulled from the oven. I am infinitely happy beneath these lavender skies, heavens bleeding into our Blue Ridge like a watercolor daydream. It is before the world wakes up. It is after darkness falls. These are mornings straight out of Rockwell paintings, Grimms' Fairy Tales, every biblical creation story translated to any language spoken by tongues like ours. It is said that, after the great design, God observed all He had made and, in splendor, remarked that it was very good. And indeed, very good are these mornings, these afternoons we spend feeling wholesomely crafted and beautifully made, shy and gorgeous creatures in a handmade, homespun world. It is a perfect morning for almost-perfect loving and I am stitched back together—by smiling babies, your dizzy laughter, our off-key singing all the way back home. These are mornings neither before nor after. Just now, just ours.

Sweet Unlikeness

What differentiates you from the rest
is that you do not love me *despite*
or even *in spite of*
but *because* of them:
all of my despites and in spite ofs
lined up like soldiers ready for war.

When I Say I Love You More Than Anything

I mean *I've traced freckle constellations on far too many bare backs to be proud of but hadn't found the right star to land on until I ran my pointer finger across yours.*

I mean *I'd give up my dreams and follow you to Sacramento. I'd pack poems in my suitcase and squeeze your hand on the red-eye and abandon my perfectly fine life to build a new one with you. I'd write from there. Or maybe I wouldn't. Maybe I'd give up writing, too.*

I mean *Sometimes I dream of keeping you in my closet but not in the serial killer kind of way. I worry about too many things. Like the world caving in and swallowing you whole.*

I mean *I love you more than anything.*

Which means *Is it the same for you?*

Would you keep me in your closet?

Would you buy that one-way ticket?

Have you found a star to land on yet?

I mean—

Is it one of mine?

Saint Valentine

It is nearing midnight and my fingers are stained pink from baking red velvet cupcakes in a bleary-eyed haze. In this airless apartment kitchen I sit contemplating the mystery of Saint Valentine, the enigmatic figure whom we have forgotten under the guise of boxed chocolates and secular festivities held dear to the heart, and how the monk's entire life was deemed, by an early pope, as "known only to God." There are multiple accounts of him, but no set truth defining his existence. No one really knows who he was. The Internet reveals to me that the man could've been two separate people, scratch that, maybe even a handful. It's kind of like the Shakespeare authorship question. Who really penned all 39 plays? We might've been calling the wrong talent "the greatest writer in the English language" for centuries. Who cares? I never really cared for the Bard anyway. Sue me. I just hope "he" wasn't a woman like me.

I only wonder because lately I've been thinking about the legacies we leave behind scattered across an ever-expanding timeline. I do not have 154 sonnets hidden under this crimson-stained apron. I am no religious icon, no roseate martyr. There will be no international holiday dedicated to the way I loved. Instead I am surrounded by spilt flour and piles of powdered sugar and my lopsided midnight creations cooling in the pan. I am half asleep and half praying these taste better than they look. Because this world will forget me. I am not extraordinary by any stretch of the imagination. But I'm here now: hunched over at the dining table, contented and breathless to be witness, human in my nature of being easily forgettable. When I am finally lost in time, when my words fade to oblivion, when I am nothing more than a space that used to be filled, know this. I lived. I lived to stay up late and live some more. I tried my damn hardest. That is the only legacy I'll ever need.

A Matter of Being

It is said that,
in the grand scheme of things,
nothing matters. We are dust
and back to dust returning.

Rinse and repeat.

But at the atomic level
we are something like forty percent
star material. No wonder you hold me
and I glow. My matter belongs
to your ancestors' ancestors,
the ground they tread upon,
their fruitful joy and fruitless despair,
and you, of course, the byproduct
of a thousand and one love stories.

You and I, we are children
of light. Descendants of
prehistoric explosions,
the hand of God descending
to mold earth's clay into arms
we now use to hold tight.

Rinse and repeat.

As long as we can clutch
we cannot dissolve.

Holy Ground

requires no great pilgrimage
nor any red-eye flight to book.
Upon arrival, there may not even
be an altar on which to offer
what is owed.

Holy ground is wherever you leave your love.

So every public bathroom stall within
which I have grieved into my hands.
A certain Catholic church basement,
still haunted by the sweaty magic of old
friends long gone, the dark wooded backroads
of my native Virginia, the humid shoebox room
I occupied my first year apart from childhood,
the grimy twin XL and cobwebbed window panes.

Holy ground is wherever love finds you again.

The back stairwell of the dilapidated classroom
building we accidentally followed last February.
The bus stop where I first kissed you, feeling
it was right. Holy ground, these moonlit paths
I walk with you, wordless, basking in starry stillness,
this sacred earth something we now share.

Loves of My Life

why must we limit ourselves to one? / love, that is / why must we singularize? / put up the white picket fence, darling / label it forever / marry it / must we always / reduce, confine, unionize? / whatever happened to freedom? / free love? / for i find myself always ending / beginning / and ending again / in these synapses of time / in the morning i fall in love with rain / by afternoon i have forgotten the downpour / and the sun woos me once more / after that i belong to the moon / only the moon / stop speaking in metaphors! / why must i / always relate love to these forces of nature? / why must i categorize it? / why must i call it beautiful? / does love ever get tired of beautiful, do you think? / the matter of fact is that i cannot stop falling / and rising in love / cannot stop my soul from bending / to meet everything that stands on its tiptoes to kiss it / some days i fall in love with the piano / i've never learned how to play / i don't have that kind of mind / but my ear could listen to her keys forever / gentle fingers / you know how to tangle me too well / why must i have one? / love, that is / and isn't, all at once / why can't i hold multiple in my palm? / loves of my life / little breathing creatures / the things that stitch me together / unravel my yarn heart / hold me in their breath / you / him / her / me / that / there / then / i love it all / twister of tongues / so why / can't i marry the world?

Trust Me

When I was younger, I thought love was hesitation.

Was constant airplane brace position, impact anticipation, miles above mountains yet already imagining the charred stench of flesh and aluminum. Was fear of flight. Thought love was crisis prevention, apocalypse preparation, stocking up on nonperishables for the end of time. Thought love was choosing words with the precision of a night shift surgeon. Knowing how much I love you, but still flipping through thesaurus pages to find the most beautiful words to *mean* it. Thought it was carefulness. Neurosis. Biting tongue to hold back from spilling too much. Because *I love you, an♦ I can't lose this. Every ♦ay I feel sicker an♦ sicker imagining all of the lives we are not living. But I love you. I love you. I will always hesitate.*

I am older now. I have realized. So much of love is blind risk. We can't live in bomb shelters forever. We can't hunch over for so long we forget to gaze out through the glass, to chase constellations and fireflies and wild dogs running through afternoon sprinklers. We can't keep surviving on the nutrition of fear. There is no substance in hiding. There is no joy in loving by the rules.

Because love is trusting the possibility of tragedy. The inevitable end. Is running the red light anyway, because *I ♦on't want to miss a single thing.* Is pouring in the milk without triple-checking the expiration date. Is mixing it in, and in, and in.

Love is handing you the car key, believing you'll come back home.

What the Mind Can't Take

On dark days, the mind steals
all it can find, stripping the body
of energy, harvesting the chance
to keep what is meant
to be kept.

Like time
and memory.

I have grown used to the sensation
of *take*, of weeping *I have nothing left*,
of standing at the precipice of madness,
my heart a vacuum, my voice depleted
of giving.

I have given so much
to so many, yet still I give

and still the mind takes.

But when I am loving you
in July and we are walking
across the Fort Pitt bridge,
your palm airtight against
my own, I command my eyes
to *Memorize this, take it all in*—
all of this peeling yellow paint,
our laughter a stone skipping
across the river. If only this bridge

arched a little bit higher, if only
we never had to peel our hands
apart. We could walk forever
that way, suspended in summer,
our voices bouncing from steel beams.

Memorize this, I whisper to myself,
an• nothing can take it away from you.

This is how I keep time
and memory—

I take it all in.
You—my brightest day,
the highest height,

are what the mind,

though it tries,

can't take.

The Cosmos Is a Romantic

I know so.

Consider the unspoken magnetism between two strangers.
Mystery charges the distance between separate bodies,
interrupting the graceful orbit between planets
never meant to collide.

All love is merely push and pull.
Potential either used or wasted.
Like energy, it cannot be created nor destroyed.
This is the great tragedy of our species, a law of our universe:
sometimes love only lasts the duration of a subway ride,
eye contact for the smallest of eternities, shared laughter
already ancient history seconds after it begins.
We can never get it back, restored to the same version,
the resurrection of a moment in full technicolor detail.
What we reimagine is never enough.
Past realities cannot be resuscitated.
We cannot breathe life into the dead.

This is not purely science, mathematical equations, theories.

It can't be.

The cosmos is a romantic.
I know because we exist.

You Make Me Want to Say Yes

to orchid centerpieces and crawling ivy
and space to dance. To heels with a crisp
click to them, a white lace A-line dress,
perhaps even some tulle, that perfect swing
of fabric when you dip me into moonlight.
You make me want to become acquainted
with champagne toasts and fine china,
my left hand sporting a heavier finger.
You make me want to *I ♦o* myself

to death. I had never before pictured
becoming that kind of woman, that
specific breed of bold. But for you,
I ♦o. You make me want to be that kind

of almost-summer afternoon, early June,
never lovelier. You make me want to meet
you at the end of every aisle—whether
it be church or grocery store or dilapidated
classroom building. *I ♦o I ♦o I ♦o.*

Meet me there, will you? Meet me
at the intersection of now and always.
You make me want to say yes
to everything in-between.

This Will Be Our Year

Somewhere spilling down the winding roads of western Pennsylvania I am with you and we are happy. I've got a good feeling about this one—Christmas lights still wrapped around the pillars of front porches, laughter so sickly sweet it burns, how we are the protagonists of our very own vintage Hallmark special. This year it's too warm for any real snow. It hardly matters, even for people like us, people who love the cinema of a perfect winter. I could do this forever, could call you home for a lifetime, *my place my person my hand to squeeze doesn't matter if we're three-hundred miles from the world I grew up in. I'll just build a new one with you.* I've got a good feeling about being twenty on the first day of this new decade, one as fresh as the winter snow blanketing someone else's front yard in another universe, not ours. Ours is warmed by the little mysteries that lie ahead, waiting for us around the corner to find them, for our hands to unwrap the *will be, one day,* beautiful unknown. Who knows what roads we'll traverse this year or the next, what seeds of love or laughter we will plant, what will become of these stoplight moments, this sunset magic, our midnight slow dances glowing. All I know is that this could be our year. This could be our life, this equitable arrangement of you and me, this could be the world we will keep.

A Box to Strike

I want nothing of passive love. Give me gore and sweat and flesh.
I do not mesh well with lukewarm, tepid-hearted temperance,
ironed-out wrinkles, spoonfuls of sugar to make it all wash down
a little easier. I hate the kind of love you have to tiptoe around,
making sure not to disturb the floorboards, avoiding eggshells.
The kind of love that cannot scream its own name, the kind
that must deliberate before making a decision—useless love!
Give me blood and heat and whiplash. Give me eager hands
that know *how* and *when* to trespass. I want to love like a child

with a match and a box to strike. Unthinking love. Burning
everything down love, the whole sky swelling in fear of itself.

Though We Live Without Order

after everything an• everyone I've ever known

I live by maps and love by stars.
Find the patterns, trail his footsteps,
follow lovers back to their homes.
Feed me sequence: *crack an egg,*
pour the flour, beat until light.
There are roles to play. Everyone
you meet is an archetype of another.
Thinking this way, I am only
an amalgamation of everything
I've seen. Hollywood starlets
of black-and-white films. Pretty
smiles on pretty girls with prettier
minds. There is no such thing
as an authentic original. Every idea
is an act of deflowering. I can try
but I only end up infringing
on someone else's copy. You
and I—we didn't invent romance.
Neither did Juliet and her dagger
or any man holding a boombox
over his head to win the girl.
But god, when you make me
break every rule I've ever written,
it sure feels a lot like we did.

Juxtaposition

A lot of things simply cannot exist together.

Cats and bubble baths.
Paperback books and spilled glasses of milk.
Love and dishonesty.
Innocence and knowledge.

The universe demands that these sets of objects
remain separate, uninvolved with each other,
divorced from all possible contact.
It is the universal law of long-distance relationships.
To intermingle them would be
to create chaos, to toy with dangerous flame.

But yet some things are made to exist together.

Sidewalk cracks and yellow dandelions.
Buttered popcorn and cinema screens.
Two sets of eager lips.
Your heart, a hummingbird
fluttering in my hands—
I knew from the moment it landed
that it was meant to live there.

I live for the things
you would not expect to exist together.
For the unexpected perfect fit—
two wrongs lining up to make a right,

opposites not only attracting, but
making sweet love out of the very
conflict of existence.

You and I.
I never expected to love you.

But I do.

I love you like waking up early
and accidentally stumbling upon sunrise.
Like random chance.
Like snow in October.
Like coming home after years
of searching everywhere to find it.
And you clutch in your hands a red carnation
so bright against the gray September rain
it could have been mistaken for fire.

A Place to Put Your Hands

Latchkey child, someday someone will take care of you.
I know you never had that. For years it was turn the key,
kick off your shoes, wait and wait and wait. It was
leftover pizza in Ziploc bags, hasty handwriting scrawled
on pages ripped from magazines. Be home late. Food in fridge. Mom.

I remember one time you cried because you never had a family.
And I did, too, because I couldn't wipe your memory
of the nights you sat there, waiting and waiting and waiting,
for something (someone?) to belong to.

I hope she opens the door before you can even reach for the doorknob.
And I hope you love with the windows flung wide open,
the front door unlocked, in a safe neighborhood
with a firm foundation and a guarded heart.
I hope it's ready for you, that life you never got:
a table already set, a pair of hands running through
the tangles in your hair, someone to come home to.
I hope you never need another key.

I hope someone is waiting for you somewhere, in the imaginary house
you'll find one day. That she stays up late, waits for you to return,
fighting the heaviness of sleep just to tuck you in
the way I would have, if I could.

Or at the very least, I hope she leaves a light on.

The Good Flesh Continuing

after Robert Hass

Our bodies are extensions of the universe. Recycled
stardust, byproducts of galactic explosions. We were
born before time. No wonder we must touch. Hands
intertwining, tangling, assuming form. To touch is to
counterfeit the feeling of coming home, rearranging
our atoms in an order that resurrects the *before* of us—
less body, less mortal, less blood. How we used to be
mere ripples in the fabric of the infinite, still unironed.

When we touch, it is the closest we get to the oneness of
our nature. It is our only map. Each scar of yours I trace
with my index finger picks up where our origin story left
off. This is how we write ourselves whole again. We touch,

we collide—over and over until our dust remembers why.

A Certain Kind

The love he gives me is the kind of love I hope everyone has the privilege of knowing at least once in their life. *That* kind of love—how he asks me to send him old photos from before I met him because "I want to see everything I missed." A Sunday kind of love, the type Etta James curls her voice to—classic, soulful, the variety that was still in vogue when our grandparents were high schoolers sharing milkshakes under the flickering neon sign of the local diner. And even before that, when lovers were torn from each other's arms by raging war. His love reveals itself in purple orchid petals collecting on my windowsill, surprise letters tucked inside white mailing envelopes, walking me home despite my protests, past midnight, every midnight, even in the dead of winter, because "I know I don't have to. I want to." I can't get enough of that heart. It eclipses every other I've held close to mine. And though we can't predict how long this new war will last, though there is no countdown until *next time* yet, when my body misses its perfect fit, he still whispers, over and over from the other end of the line that connects our voices, "It doesn't matter how long it takes. I will meet you there. I will." For now, I keep sending him the photos he asked for, traveling back in time to *before us,* all the while knowing I wouldn't return to those memories if the world depended on it, that this life we now share, this *cook-you-dinner, meet-my-family love,* is the only one still worth choosing, framing, never blinking for even a split second in fear of what could be lost within that interval. I still don't know how to tell him. He didn't miss a single thing.

20/20

I fall in love
at least a hundred times
each day. Simplicity
latches onto my heartstrings,
frayed as they are,
and suddenly
I am enamored, colored
burgundy and catching glimpses
of celestial beings.
A perfect combination of
sleep deprivation, stairwells
slippery from yesterday's rain,
rose-colored grapes squelching
between the hollows of my teeth.
Quiet acquaintances leave me breathless.
Stumbling, my giddy-pitted stomach
flutters to the half-steps
of barefoot dancing. I have fallen
headfirst, tipsy for each color
slipping subconsciously behind
the retinas of humans who have
never bothered to look twice.
I am not like them.
I am, instead, always looking,
loving—the dusty reds and blues written
on the hands of strangers.

There Are Answers and There Are Questions

It's moments like these, eyes locked under the subtle glow of lamp posts, that I remember why.

Earlier today we made lemon chicken and baked cinnamon apples and I watched as you stood in my apartment kitchen, whistling to yourself as you cooked, and remembered why.

And then we cozied up under my floral quilt and talked sleepily about marriage and God and what variety of magic it takes to reach both of those grand entities. Again, I remembered why.

There are answers and there are questions.

I am constantly consumed by the latter.

Do we pick who we love? Is there any way of knowing for sure?

Did I make the right choice when I picked you?

You,

over-seasoning the vegetables we'd sliced for dinner,

nuzzling up against my neck and scheming about one day,

walking me home hand-in-hand across the silent streets,

are the answer to my infinite *why*.

Critical Moments of Convincing Faith

What makes love matter lies at the atomic level, in matter itself.

Daring graze on a quivering thigh,

eager trace of the vertebrae, a slipped fabric *please!*

then a sensation of holiness, guilty baptism, both of us glowing godly

in the ungodly. You clutch me and I hold back *Amen,*

as if your act of doing so could be mistaken for prayer.

The turning points of every great love are buried in the gray mundane.

Too often omitted, accidentally overlooked until after

the resolution, when the other half of the bed becomes its own winter,

and no one is there to laugh at you when your hair falls into your ketchup

like when we would sit in the back booth of the filthy McDonald's

condemning the sins of capitalism and American consumerism

and we are taking short turns sipping flat soda from the same straw

and cracking up until the amber liquid stings its way out of our nostrils, and we are almost crying for countless reasons

like snorting soda and inescapable classism and how foolish it is

to lose your virginity on a dorm room bed and how *Pulp Fiction*

is overrated, the subject of far too many brainless intellectual debates

and how neither of us want to say the thing we are both thinking,

the words to make it all materialize,

that will give our blessed love a skeleton and skin and organs capable of

rupturing, both of us refusing to claim responsibility for giving form

to this breathing thing we share, that we know to be true, our bodies

becoming real, every small movement repeating *Amen, Amen, Amen.*

A Love Letter

to the way your clothes smell after a full day:
sweat, almond-scented body wash, detergent—

to the way you cannot sleep without twitching—

to the pale white scar on your left eyebrow from
falling out of bed as a hyperactive three-year-old—

to your middle-child mind—

to the way you sing in falsetto to make me laugh
and the worst part is, it's not even half bad!—

to the yellow bridges that populate the skyline
of the city where you grew up—

to the God you believe in—

to your annoying tendency to listen selectively—

to the way you can't dance
and yet choose to dance with me anyway—

to all of the ways
you are—

Homesick for Another World

after Ottessa Moshfegh

I don't try to relate. There's no use. There are billions of brilliant minds and then there's mine, which isn't brilliant nor dull, but somewhere adrift in the dusky in-between. I'm too much of everything and too little of what actually matters. Too much emotion, too little control of it. Too much panic, too little reason for it. In the company of others, I feel almost alien, as if I possess a quality still unknown to me that repels, that turns heads the other direction out of terror. Like the part of the horror movie before the jump scare, before the killer finds the sleeping starlet talking in her sleep. I'm bug-eyed and awkward and better alone. I'm uncomfortable in togetherness, unstable in love, nervous no matter whose arms I rest in. In another life I can breathe. I can let peace just be peace, love just be love. I can hold your hand without tensing up when you loosen your grip. I can speak loud enough for your friends to hear me, can order my own food at the restaurant, can small-talk any stranger. And I'm jealous of the other kinds of minds—minds that would not willingly choose death over being known—jealous of the souls that sparkle without dreading the burden of being seen. I love cold wind that numbs the fingertips and the corners of bustling train stations perfect for poetry and being comfortably alone with you. I love indoor cats observing passersby through the windows of my parochial universe and rundown beach boardwalk shops with the terribly sexist T-shirts and squeezing your hand in the passenger seat. I love that you love me in spite of my fear of being loved. And that you stay with me, when I'm choking on air, and my mind becomes a haunted house, and I'm weeping in the spare room of your family beach house because the world is too loud for my liking, and I'm one break-down away from a hospital stay. That you choose me, that you choose me, that you choose me—when I'm homesick for another world but this is the only one that we'll ever know.

If the Perfect Person

were to walk straight into the marrow of my life,

I'd tell him to leave.

Pack your bags, walk backwar♦s out of that ♦oor like a movie playe♦ in reverse an♦ back to whatever fairy tale you manage♦ to escape. I want nothing to do with perfect. Spare me the drama of happily ever after. I wouldn't want the perfect person if the universe had measured him for me. I am light years away from sainthood.

I want everything to do with you. You and your aching and your real and your raw. You and the wetness dampening the apples of your cheeks. You and the lawless way you crumble, how you shatter in my hands. You on a Tuesday night when our world unravels and we have no language, only bodies that can somehow, in spite of the odds, still weep and dance under flickering lampposts. You, when you dance with me anyway, when there are no words left to say, no meanings we can find under any sort of light, only my head on your chest and no music other than *trust, trust, trust.* You, when, out of the both of us, it is only your heartbeat that can still speak.

Yes, I would tell him to leave. This heart is only for you and your sick and your sweat and your grief. You when it is easy and when it is hard and when it is beyond all feeling, when we have to trade emotion for knowledge, when we do not know what tomorrow will bring but choose to stand there, twenty degrees in the middle of January, with arms wide open and nothing left but love to carry us through. We are not saints nor perfect martyrs. We are two shivering shadows in a world beyond explanation, clutching onto something as holy as hope.

Bloodlines

You are the byproduct of your *great great great an*♦ *maybe*
even greater grandparents' first kiss. In the equation of history
you are the long-awaited answer. You transcend all laws
of mathematics. Their history bent you into existence.

Consider it for a moment. You are only here because
one man saw, from across a train platform or mossy field
or crowded ballroom, a strange beauty with a flicker
lodged in her eye. *Don't min*♦ *if I catch it,* he told himself,
and he did. The possibility of you—conceived in the rash decision
of a moment. Now you have her eyes, same unusual twinkle,
the fruit of a great pursuit. Yes, you were born before your mother
carried your body to earth. You were born, instead, in the instant
of the first chase, the swift clutch of a hand, the rush of blood to the face.

Think. If not for the speeding train. The field. The ballroom and the girl,
still a stranger, the mumbled-under-breath *Don't min*♦ *if I catch it.*

Then—the universe caught you. Forever the echo.
Forever the beginning, you have always been.

Vignettes on Almost-Summer

I.

Under the five o'clock sun, when both the sky and the swimming pool bleed out the same hypnotizing shade of blue, I feel happiness for the first time all spring.

II.

I'm staying in a white-pillared beach house two streets away from the Atlantic Ocean with a family that feels like mine. In the morning, I wake up before everyone to sit by the bay window, armed with black coffee and fatigue, just to listen to the wind. It beats upon the awning, desperate for attention. And so I give it my full.

III.

Sunburnt shoulders and bikini tan lines, long walks to the pier clutching hands and not letting go, fleeing the hot tub just to cannonball into the fifty-degree pool in midnight freezing rain. In the ocean I let the colossal waves carry my body, limp and willing to surrender, out of the riptide and back to shore.

IV.

I like the way I look in the pictures you take of me when I'm wearing my best black dress and we're walking in the wet sand under a vague lavender sky and you stop me because it's golden hour and you want to capture me happy, hair windswept and in my eyes. I like seeing myself happy. It's like traveling across the ocean just to step foot in an ancient land, just to be able to say I did.

V.

I don't want to go home. I don't want to be without you again.

I Am No Angel

but the woman who loves you. As far
removed from celestial as the word
itself permits. No divine messenger
shrouded in starlight, nothing sinless
nor unstained. I do not speak their
language of perfect holiness, that
mocking, heavenly song. I am no
angel. I have never fallen from those
great heights. Love, this flesh, do you
feel its wickedness, pregnant
with earth? When you taste me,
do I leave your tongue marred
with soil? These shoulder blades
never grew wings, refusing, no matter
how many nights my small frame
crumpled in prayer for them.
I have never indulged in flight nor
freedom, have never rescued a soul
in peril. The closest I have ever
come is this act of clutching
you, dear heart, these mortal arms,
warming your bones with the beat
of my heart, all blood and evil
ancestry, my love a clot that holds.
I am no angel, precious thing,
but in these finite human moments
in which we are animals keeping warm,
nothing but fallible material, newborn

creatures yet to be washed clean from
the origin of our birth and still fresh
from the hidden womb, I come close,
my love, I come close.

Opalescence

I suppose I could write about the color of your eyes
pale blue with a gold ring surrounding the pupil
or how the sky looked at eight o'clock this evening
pink-streaked, cotton candy, like sugar spun by hand
or how electric I felt, strolling back from the bus stop
crimson red, set aflame, a wailing siren for a heart
leaving you behind, boarding for the dying day
your departure left a diamond in my hands, translucent
and all I knew is a feeling sat lodged in my throat
a precious stone? a piece of obsidian? an opal?
but not precisely a feeling, but something missing
yes, an opal: iridescent, like stained glass catching the light
I should have said something, I should have said I love you
red orange yellow green blue indigo violet and more
because that is all I could think of, I love you
choking on the bright flecks of rainbow
all the way back home, I love you.

For You I Would Jump First

I cannot love carefully.

Unlike you, I do not prepare for it. You are *knee pads* and *escape plan* and *desperate Sign of the Cross*. You triple-check and strategize and never leap without certainty of safety. I am not like you. I am *free-fall* and *blind faith* and *trusting the parachute without checking to see if it is even tethered to my body at all.*

You love me anxiously. I love you recklessly.

It is hard, reconciling this. I cradle you closer than skin and dream of our house by the bay, pale yellow shutters and little ones in the yard, picking weeds and gathering ladybugs. Sunday mornings, cross-country road trips to the canyons, to the other ocean, I see it all with you. You keep your eyes shut, lashes flitting, lost in some other dream.

You fear making a mistake out of eagerness, miscalculation, too much risk. I fear not risking enough. For you I put all of my eggs in one basket and swing, letting time decide the trajectory. I do not fear the landing. I would rather trust gravity than waste potential.

I cannot love with reservations.

But you do and you can. You calculate the geometry of your plunge. You are *seatbelts* and *weighing consequences* and *guarantee.* But I still love you. I can jump first, nosediving without a net to catch me, my dilapidated body waiting at the bottom just to give you a safe place to land.

Quid Pro Quo

The way we love is *qui♦ pro quo.* I'll give you mine
if you give me yours. We are keen on exchanging
parts of wholes: my nimble fingers on your spine
for a soft pillow to lay my head upon, your free
time for my girlish laughter, my trivial poems for
even the smallest fraction of your heart. Give and take,
sow and reap. We love in the language of fair trading.

Dearest part to whole, if I could I would give you everything
for nothing in return. My favorite records, my best words
all dressed up and sparkling in their Sunday best. I'd tie
curly ribbons around every memory of ours held together
by tacky Christmas wrapping paper and translucent tape.
For you I'd deem every day a holiday, bake bread by hand,
finger-paint you pictures to hang on your refrigerator door.
I'd love you like a child still loves life, how nothing can rain
on that constant sunshine parade. I'd give it all to you

in a heartbeat. No strings attached. No terms or conditions.
Just the privilege of always hearing yours, on and on,
that sweet music of needing nothing else.

Homecoming

It is hard living on the edges of things. Try building a home on the precipice of a cliff. Tell me you wouldn't live in constant fear of a sudden tectonic shift. I have learned that, when the body needs to be held, it makes a big deal of making sure the need is known. The body demands the security of a tender touch. Perhaps this is why, trembling outside your front door this morning, I felt my heart pounding straight through every insulated layer of my winter coat. I swore the buttons would snap, that my insides would spill out all over your steps, my pathetic *need* collecting in human puddles at your feet. I have learned that, when the heart needs to be tended to, it cannot stop itself from screaming. It is true; the heart never grows up. It is born young and stays young, a perpetual infant forever in need of being held to another chest. The heart cannot live at the edge of love. It is driven to madness by the need to be pursued. This is why, when you finally opened the door, my heart pacified. As if it knew yours would steady mine— no shifting, no need to scream, no cliffhanger required— just you and yours and me and mine. Try building a home in someone else's heart. Tell me you wouldn't live a little easier.

Maybe I Would Pixelate

I like to talk about things
like whether or not God would have friends
if He went to my old high school
and how all saints were probably secret skeptics
with blasphemous diary entries and how
I'd rather choke myself to death than marry someone stupid.

You don't.

You'd rather listen, absorbing my farfetched philosophies,
nodding just to gratify my sickness. I get too swept away in passion,
but you find it charming or exotic or something, I'm still not sure—
but you haven't left yet and that's what makes you different
from everyone else. You tolerate,
at the very least, my diatribes and ramblings, my red-in-the-face
awakenings that leave me breathless and murdered
on your bedroom carpet, muttering *Holy shit* over and over again
into my hands like litany. You don't articulate your opinions
on whether the universe is benevolent or indifferent or evil,
or if you believe money is merely a social construct
invented to control us like I do,
or if you're even remotely afraid of dying.

I used to hate it, wished that you'd get bloodthirsty for answers
like me, violent for truth palpable enough to hold in your palms.
But now I understand you'd rather just hold me, would rather
just swaddle me in stillness, or maybe you're afraid
that if you verbalized your inner world mine would disintegrate,

that I'd fracture into a thousand pieces, that maybe I would pixelate
in your arms. You don't say much but you don't have to.

I can feel what you're thinking without words,

when you pull me closer, into the act which requires no explanation,
no language, no absurd fit of anger to express its depths.
In these moments you're not thinking about God or money
or really anything at all—other than how to keep me
from swimming too far from shore.

The Themes Are Always the Same

after Joan Di∙ion

And maybe our world really *is* tired of love poems.

Maybe every romantic trope rots on life support.
Maybe every storybook fairy tale has already perished.

This world begs poets to bury them. Seal the tomb.
Prepare a bottomless grave for every lovestruck Romeo.
Embellish a pretty urn for every Juliet staying up late
waiting for him. The end of love has been arriving
for centuries. Maybe it already happened while poets
were too busy scrawling elegies for lovers not yet lost.

If anyone held a funeral for love poems I wasn't invited.
If anyone held a great memorial for human passions
no one showed me the photos. And thankfully so.
I am far too obsessed with this world to ever fall
out of maddening love with it. The themes might
always be the same: love, loss, life, death, but
I don't mind. It's still a world where poets burn
the midnight oil to preserve moments that would
otherwise fizzle out and die. A world where I am
allowed to witness it all, every bruised and tired
archetype, where I am allowed to believe in illusion.

The Death of Rationality

I will never be ashamed by the gravity of which I manifest my love. I've heard others mumble their concerns. That my way of doing it equates to placing a butcher knife into the fleshy hands of a small child in roller skates perched atop a sloping driveway. My love *an acci*ent waiting to happen*. My love *the potential of *isaster given wheels*. But when it comes to you I do not obey reason. I refuse to. If I did I'd be a mortal of immeasurable foolishness. What I'm saying is I don't care what their voices whisper. It's white noise to me, an ambient hum in the background I can choose to ignore. I want to love you like murdering rationality. Like not thinking twice about believing in forever. Like being deemed *illogical* and *unrealistic* and *capricious.* They will laugh. They will complain through gritted teeth. They will grow to hate how I chase what isn't mine yet.

But I planned our wedding down to the centerpieces and floral arrangements the first time I saw you. I sat down next to you and saw us growing old on the backs of my eyelids. I named our children before I ever stepped foot in your childhood room. And I don't care. I am not ashamed.

I am the woman that loves you and this is how I will.

There Was Hope for a Poem Tonight

But staying in your arms seemed far more important
than grappling for what cannot be held in words.

There are moments in time when words do not satisfy.
Instances where the body resists language and analogy,
when all it needs is to be kept safe from the dangers
of analysis, *this means this means this means this.* Enough
of that, just keep me close, who gives a damn, this is life
and I want to spend it with you, definitely and indefinitely,
without any acts of interpretation that could rage and ruin
this magic we hold, so no, not tonight. Poetry rests.

Tonight I am being kept.

Deluge

after F. Scott Fitzgerald

There are infinitely many kinds of love in this world.

There's Mom's extra fluffy chocolate chip pancakes on a lazy Sunday morning after mass. There's "Did you get home safe?" and "I won't leave until I see you lock the door behind you." There's love that stays for good and love that leaves its shirts neatly folded in your bottom drawer. There's love that comes back with a different face, somehow foreign—no, it's the same one, just older. There's kindergarten love, trading juice boxes at the very top of the playground slides. There's first love that will leave you dizzy and disoriented, eighteen years with no compass. There's love squeezing your hand tight in the ICU wing, hooked up to humming oxygen tanks. There's love with a wet tongue and floppy ears. There's love on a speeding train, sticking its hand out the window, going, going, gone, and never touched again.

Never the same love twice, said someone important somewhere. Never the right kind of batter to recreate those dewy mornings. Never enough laundry washes to get the smell out of the cotton.

Never the same face, always changing, even after a lifetime of knowing it.

Clenched Fist

You can part ways with love on a curbside, crowded train station platform, or bustling airport terminal, but it will always follow you home. And when it does, it hollows out a gaping hole into the dead center of your sternum that stings like hydrogen peroxide in an oozing wound and then leisurely festers. That's where love decides to live and that's where you are for now, while you're apart from me. Distance, I've learned, is a clenched fist in the chest without the following attack. An open mouth with no scream. A door with no knob to turn. You left my house today and I felt the stitches rip open again. You turned the street corner and I felt an artery begin to hemorrhage. And then you were out of sight and I felt the whole system fail. It's as if the body requires another body to keep its seams sewn shut. So I wait for you, spilling out, overflowing with the heavy, eager thing that followed me home.

When I Tell You I Am Trying to Be a Better Person

What I really mean is I've been biting my tongue
so hard I've left a sore so deep it hurts to speak.
Karma from the universe, I suppose. She has
a knack for double-checking that she gives back
what is owed. What I mean is I am trying to be
more easy moonlight, soft velvet of a beagle's ears.
More rocking chair on a chilly August evening,
graceful flight of a hummingbird, vanishing.

If poverty is having a soul predisposed to hate,
I have nothing in my pockets. I have burned all
the way through the fabric and my spare change
has long ago spilled onto the grimy floor of some
subway station. When I tell you I am trying
to be a better person, I mean forgiveness is not
programmed in my nature. I am more raging inferno
than rush of water. I could never become a cloistered
nun, could never obey that vow of silence. I tell you

I am trying to be a better person. Because for you I'd unclench
my jaw, loosen my death grip, relax my fist. I adore you
enough to give peace a try. To be your hummingbird
heart, soft velvet, easiest moonlight you'll ever know.

Ultraviolet

Veins constellate your eyelids,
miniature flashes of lightning.
When you blink, you storm
the parts of my soul unseen.
Purple like summer plums,
grape jelly on toasted wheat
with the crusts cut off. You
glow as tenderly as a new
bruise. I bask in it carefully,
trying not to disturb you.

I long for your royal light,
your interstellar touch.
All of my stars dance in
the wake of your gravity,
my sweet Andromeda.

Pull me closer.
I'd orbit you always.

If only you were just
a few light years closer.

If I Could

I would feed you joy on a silver spoon.

I would make you paper kites and breakfast past midnight and origami fish to hang from your ceiling.

I would heal the parts of you that shattered when you were too young to know how to reassemble the pieces.

I would do anything to watch the corners of your mouth lift and stay. Color flooding skin, painting it.

There's too much tragedy in this world, you told me once. No need for further explanation. I could see it in your eyes. You captured your past in one sentence.

I remember wanting to clothe you in light. To wrap your fingers around each of my individual heartbeats, to have you feel them pulsing between your palms. I wanted to fill you with goodness. Sweet tea and blanket forts and firefly summers in the suburbs. A father's hand and an open road and enough fight in you to find where it ends.

If I could, I would take you there.

And I'd watch you run, all the while thinking *There's too much wonder in this world*, lungs filling up with it.

Stray Weed

I can't marry a white picket fence. It's not in my nature,
to keep the roses blushing, the house tidy enough for
the neighbors to *ooh* and *ahh,* not a stray weed in sight.

I'm not a good person. Well, scratch that—maybe I am,
just not in your way. You like to sit in the front pew
at church. I like looking out the window, questioning

the essence of God, whether he really is the white man
on the laminated prayer cards they give away at funerals.
You've never wanted to die. I've watched my ending play

too many times to stay for the actual credits. Bathtub.
Car fire. Even my own mind, hand trembling in horror.
You like roses. They've always reminded me of eternal rest.

I am the stray weed, the fire, the skeptic, and the movie.
But I'd marry you, not for the fence, but because of how
I don't want to die when I'm with you. I want to live.

Lock and Key

My heart is a clenched fist
and it lives in my stomach.
In its grip dwells the scent
of green apple shampoo
from damp brown hair.
Other things, too, like
the golden halo circling
your cobalt iris, Jupiter's
fifth ring. There is also
the soft chip in your cry,
the crack that breaks me.
I hold all of these trifling
nothings between palms
like gospel. I am devoted
to keeping them under
lock and key. Consider
this a love letter to all
the cryptic parts of you
unknown to every soul
but mine. No one else
knows you hate winter
and cherry tomatoes
and that you grew up
restricted from crying
because boys cannot,
not strong ones. But
I think you're strong
and my grip on you

is even stronger—
sweet dove, let me
safekeep each piece
of you. I will not
let your tears spill
through my hands.

Not Even Blood

In my mind's eye, you're there—
it's a thousand tomorrows away and we're driving to the hospital
because our second kid's busted an eyelid on her *big girl* bed frame
when we were too occupied with fixing breakfast to notice the slip.
You are composed, outlandishly calm despite the torrent of red
soaking the kitchen rags pressed to the face of a screaming child.
This is no surprise. You were made for this sort of thing.
I already know, years before the scene can even take place,
how you would react to this minor calamity.

Fear could kill me.
I'm not like you.

You can keep your eyes on the road, expertly maneuvering
through rush hour traffic. Nothing fazes you,
not even blood. In my mind's eye, you're there—

both hands on the wheel and I'm only focused on you
from the passenger seat like you're our savior, our god,
at the very least some kind of angel.

Fear could kill me.

Not the fear of death, or bleeding out, or crashing the car,
but the fear that, in your mind's eye,

I'm not there.

Like Teeth Colliding

A celestial sort of peace invades me, resting in the hollow of your frame for the first time in one-hundred days. Simple as slipping back into an old skin, I melt noiselessly into your mold, as mindless as pulling into the driveway of a distant life. You look taller, arms fuller, eyes a paler shade of sky. But this, I know, is only love's illusion, magic orchestrated by a mind madly consumed with missing you. I love you like teeth colliding. Like eagerness and goosebumps. Like a waist pulled close. I think to myself, aching for stillness, *poetry ◦oesn't suffice anymore*, because it doesn't. It couldn't. Because when you tuck me into your cavernous spaces I'm breathless and numb and the story, the only one worth telling, can write itself.

I Am Driven Wild

by the need to be known. I am not talking
billboards or spotlights or glorious acclaim.
I'd give all of that a whirl but then surrender it
for a deep-set pair of eyes capable of predicting
the sway of my silhouette before it catches light.
For a sturdy set of hands that know how to trace
the geography of myself without folded paper
roadmaps or owner's manuals or test drives.
I do not care if this earth ever hears my name.
I do not wish to be worshipped like a distant god;
it is not in my nature to become a holy icon.
Just pull me closer. Know me like second language.
Like coming home as a child, late June and dizzy
on firefly dusk, mother's voice calling smoothly
through the flimsy screen of the kitchen window.
It is time. Know me as a place of endless returning.
Know me in the same way the wild knows you.

In Memory of Dreams

In loving memory of those we lost to the Virginia Tech shootings on April 16, 2007. May our beloved Hokies live on forever.

1.

and the feet that once walked the same paths mine do.

2.

back when the sixteenth of april was just monday,

3.

we never had to consider roses or candlelight vigils.

4.

we didn't have to.

5.

time had not yet fallen from innocence,

6.

still unplucked fruit ripening on the branch

7.

because *things like that* don't happen in *a place like this*

8.

or at least that's what everyone thought

9.

until the *things like that* happened on this very ground

10.

which all of a sudden did not feel solid anymore

11.

and the whole world watched that morning

12.

melt into mourning, into itself,

13.

leaving no words behind

14.

in all of that lacking.

15.

the most honest tragedy of this

16.

was not even the sight of blood

17.

but the anxious mother at the other end of the call

18.

waiting on words to make sense of silence.

19.

it is hard enough to watch your child leave

20.

for something like college, I know.

21.

I saw my mother cry when I packed up my room.

22.

but how do you reconcile that hurt

23.

with the hurt of these mothers:

24.

see you Thanksgiving, Christmas, Easter

25.

but all of a sudden there were no more days

26.

much less holidays. no coming back home.

27.

how do you learn to set 4 places at the table instead of 5

28.

how do you smile at stories of other people

29.

living out their dreams, knowing full well

30.

that these thirty-two never got to wake up from theirs?

31.

every day I wake up here

32.

I realize how much that matters.

Stringy Cheese and Conversation

Tonight is the eve of my nineteenth birthday.

All four of my college friends surround me,
sprawled about on the floor of a perpetually humid dorm room.
Someone's ordered two giant boxes of the best pizza in town
and we have enough room in our stomachs to finish both.

This might not seem like a lot.

After all, it's just stringy cheese and conversation
and watching whatever we can find on the TV plugged into the wall.
There's no explosion of celebration, no bottoms-up rebellion,

no extra noise.

We're just five tired kids lying on a carpet in the middle of autumn.
We have better places to be but also nowhere to go. So we stay.

It is my nineteenth birthday and I could be out dancing or falling in love
with a stranger I won't remember come sunrise. I could be
hitting the town with five of my closest girl friends in sequined dresses
and wine-stained lips, snapping photos of kisses on cheeks.
I could be so many places and so many people but instead I am here,
I am me, and somehow I am so full of love I could cry.

I don't want to be anywhere else but here, so I stay.

I never planned on nineteen years, on making it to this high of a number written in frosting on a cake, on getting past the year of frozen beaches and bad haircuts and even worse decisions.

I never planned on surviving eighteen, never planned on staying this long.

So I stay. We stay. This is how we all celebrate tonight: we all stay.

IV

WHISPERED
EXPLOSIONS

This Unearthly Glow

I private-message my poet friend. *I want our worl• back.*

Almost instantly, she replies. *I want our worl• back too.*

I say *It feels so •ifferent. Something feels change•. Can't
pinpoint what. Like energy, a strange invisible movement.*

*As if there's been a fun•amental shift out in the universe
an• we are lost in ripples on the outer e•ge,* she responds.
Then, something to cleanse the palate. *You'• like Oregon.*

I've always wante• to go there. Very cinematic, I answer.
For a moment I dream of somewhere new to me. *But no,
I un•erstan•. Something cosmic feels terribly misaligne•.
I've never been this existentially fearful. There's a •eep-
roote• anxiety that feels weir•ly apocalyptic.* I think of
Oregon. I think of my poet friend and our old world.

She counters, *Like the calm right before a storm we've
never ha• before. Settle• in a state of •iscomfort.* Then,
I think I'm gonna go cry in the shower now. I double-tap
her message. This is how scared kids express solidarity.

These are the days for standing beneath streams of water
and weeping, panicked by what unknown Armageddon
might already be crowning. *Corona:* in anatomical terms
a part of the body resembling a crown. In astronomical
terms, a glowing envelope surrounding our sun and stars.

What blinds our sight? What crowns from our bodies? What surrounds us in this way that cannot be seen nor perceived, this way that leaves poets without language?

Private Practices

8:30 AM, more or less— wake up halfway, stay in bed a few minutes longer, refresh the trending page on whatever stupid app my finger finds first. (pretend to) be shocked by death toll reports (higher than yesterday, and the day before, and the day before, and... you get the picture). gloss over words like *shortage* and *front lines* and *essential workers.* scan the obituaries. clear app eventually. find myself already yearning for a new day.

11:00 AM— eat breakfast in an attempt to fill the black hole of hopelessness churning in the pit of my stomach. realize that never works—not these days, at least. do some light aerobic exercises to remember that I somehow still have a body. might as well remind myself, right? take a scalding hot shower to melt whatever self-pity still contaminates my skin, then either sob in there or perform the most dramatic songs on my quarantine playlist, because I still can do both of those things, if anything at all.

2:00 PM— angst kicks in. throw a mental tantrum and fantasize about the void.

4:00 PM— do something, anything. today, for example: jump on the basement trampoline for an hour just to feel something other than anchored down. smile at the dust particles dancing in the light. remember, even for a moment, that I am part of a grand waltz.

6:00 PM— watch the reporter on TV tear up as he wraps up the evening news. remember again that I am part of a grand waltz, except none of us can hear the music anymore.

8:00 PM— try to write a poem. realize I can't do anything but beat myself up over the act of not being able to do so. grapple for the right words, or even words at all. such feats feel impossible under these bleak skies, these horror film evenings. all I can do is sit there, as vacant as the street outside my window.

9:30 PM— get mad. really mad. say some things about my life I don't really mean. I really am grateful to be here. some people don't even have that anymore.

11:00 PM— calm down. at least a little bit.

12:00 AM— say something quietly to myself. *look, a new ιay!* or *look... a new ιay.* the tone varies.

1:00 AM— try to fall asleep.

2:00 AM— try harder.

3:00 AM, more or less— last thought I have before the lights shut off for the night: *time will tell.*

So I Let Myself Cry

at the videos of people singing in unison from their balconies
in full belief that only music can stop this war and I let myself
mourn the images of ransacked grocery store aisles, someone's
mother weeping because there's nothing left but new language
called *fear of the unknown* and because we can't clutch hands,
not yet, which is all I need when I wake and the world feels more
like a burning corpse and less like the one we remember and so
I let my heart break just like that—like the seams of the earth
suddenly ripped wide open, every great triumph and tribulation
bleeding onto the vacant streets we once wandered when we were
still kids, still giggling vessels of hope, still innocent enough to trust
the safety of the stitching, that promise of freedom unthreatened.

I love you so I let myself cry over the lack of you. Over the memory
of the place we once shared, when it was still as good as the day God
breathed it real, the rolling hills and the fog and the infinity of touch,
feel, taste. *Look around. It's ours and nothing can change that, not now,*

not yet, not ever.

In Search Of

My iPhone 11 reports that my Screen Time has shot up 15% since last
week, with a Daily Average of 13 hours and 12 minutes. That's more than
50% of one earthly rotation, over half of the whole damn pie, and yet I
still don't bother setting fancy App Limits or Downtime or anything of
the sort. This is no time for deprivation. This is time for despair. Tonight
I watched my favorite artists' Vevo music videos from the comfort of my
outgrown twin bed, nightly mug of green tea fixed on my nightstand. It
got cold within minutes. I was too busy absorbing a wavy-haired Lorde
dance and writhe on a Jamaican beach, clad in flowing color for her song
"Perfect Places" from 2017's *Melo•rama,* a dizzying masterpiece of a show
I was lucky enough to catch live in D.C. at 18, my first ever big-girl con-
cert. After, I watched Mitski's surreal "Nobody," a statement piece hot off
her latest record, *Be The Cowboy,* which I admittedly looped for an entire
summer during my two-hour commute to the city for my first corporate
gig. I felt, then and now, too much like the girl in the video, trapped in a
candy-colored escape room with no exit, too bright, too angsty, too iso-
lated. I continued like this for hours. Weyes Blood's "Movies" from *Ti-
tanic Rising,* the only vinyl that seems to find itself spinning on my
Crosley these days, her voice the one atemporal, '60s-reminiscent siren
sound I can't get sick of. I watched five times over and felt as if I were as-
tral projecting, or at least I couldn't stop myself from imagining it. Then
again, for the haunting Julia Jacklin in her simple suburban beauty, and
the ever-enrapturing Lana Del Rey suspended from a bridge. All of these
women doing their thing and there I was, doing mine: observing, taking
in, spellbound.

This is no time for deprivation. This is time for despair. After surfacing
from the depths of my great musical plunge, I decided to look up random

garbage on the mud-bath that is the Internet, namely, Mr. Google him-self. These days Google masquerades as God, and that man is famous for knowing everything. So I tested him. I looked up *COVID-19.* After proba-bly 6 full seconds of panicked scanning, I promptly thumbed through Set-tings in an attempt to block the phrase from ever appearing on my screen again. I couldn't figure it out so I made a mental note right there to just tune out for good. *I'm sick of this,* I greeted the search engine once more. *About 538,000,000 results (0.56 secon٠s),* the fake deity apathetically re-ported. But nothing I was looking for. In a nihilistic fury, I texted An-drew, *what the hell, why can't I be with you yet?* Pressed send. It delivered. Waited for the response, got it after seconds. *Soon,* he said. *So soon.*

A WANTED ad I'd nail to every corner of my hometown if we were al-lowed to roam outside:

Looking for a girl, 5'5, unkempt hair, bad posture, clunky overbite that never got corrected even after years of orthodontic work. Anyway, I re-ally need to find her. I still need to take her to those concerts, to a church where people shake hands and God is still God and not God Google, to the open arms of the boy who loves her from 350 miserable miles away, to a city so packed she has no choice but to rub sweaty shoulders with strangers, but I know she'll love it anyway, the comfort of fitting perfectly into a world that wants her back, that holds her close, that moves her blood. A world that wants her in it.

Reward:

I don't know. *A cup of tea? Music to cry to?* Whatever's left. Something good.

Then We'll Be Happy We Made It

Maybe when the air cools, and it's mid-October
and the farmers market stands are lined with jars
of homemade apple butter, and the whole earth
lurches forward in steady motion again, children
cart-wheeling and climbing and pleading for five
more minutes in the dying sun, receiving the nod
of approval and screeching *You're it!* to unfreeze
their endless game of catch-me-if-you-can, and the
movie theaters open their doors for fifteen-year-olds
on clammy-handed first dates, when we can wipe
hysterical, stitch-in-the-side tears from each other's
faces, when the doctors can come home satisfied
with "just another day on the job," when small eyes
can peer out of small airplane windows, thousands
of feet up in the blue, when we can stop trimming
our shirts to fashion barriers to block the bad air,
when we can finally relearn how good it is to touch,
to tremble, to clutch each other so tightly we burst
blood vessels in the passion of doing so, when it's
safe enough to do all the things we swore we'd do
when we were young enough to believe any of it
could ever get taken away, when we finally do
those things and let our bodies tread in the waters
of sensation, when I have you and you have me,
maybe it can just be October, just a good day.

If Not For

Meanwhile the world goes on—

and gap-toothed children still go about believing in
Santa Claus and closet monsters and imaginary friends.
The birds still sing their same tune from the treetops as
if they have no clue what sort of world we now live in, or
maybe they do and this is just their way of pretending not.
It would be so easy to give up on a dying world if not for
these flickers of promise: azalea bush outside my window
blooming in scarlet, drumbeat in my chest begging me to
Stay, stay, stay. It's springtime and I'm hollow but innocence
grows everywhere. Sprouts are rising from my garden pots and
soon it will be warm and I'll be next to you again. The wait will
be worth its while. In the meantime, people will be people and
I'll still be the writer, observer of this holy unraveling: stars that
choose to take their place in the heavens no matter who sticks
around to see them, or who doesn't, or who can't. This life does
not perform for anyone, not me, not you. It just is.
Meanwhile the world goes on—

and I stop to listen
to its quiet music,
infinitely looping.

Contact Without Consequences

Tell me it'll end well.

Tell me we'll sit criss-cross applesauce on wall tapestries fashioned into makeshift beach towels until the August sun bleeds purple dye onto our sweaty thighs.

Tell me we'll make it to the cities forever unchecked on our bucket lists, that we'll take on the streets clutching clammy hands and not worrying if the shoulders of strangers bump into ours without apology. That if someone clears their throat we won't turn the corner or evacuate the sidewalk, we'll just keep walking and the conversation will, too.

Tell me it'll end with our friends piled on top of each other, a singular giggling mass in the center of the apartment rug, that we'll be the sun in our own solar system again, that gravity will tether us together and not further out of orbit.

I miss touching without thinking. Contact without consequences. Pinky promises and deafening stadiums and the pink birthday candles I never got to watch my best friend blow out. I miss blushing at coffee shops on rainy Saturdays when the characters in my novel finally share more than just a glance across a crowded room.

A crowded room. That feeling of being held. Of being alone but never lonely.

Real life has no proper replica. No suitable alternative.

You and I, the ones we love, the world we share.

Tell me we'll get it back.

Anno Domini

Have you ever thirsted for a return to innocence?
Here is our land—iron red and tainted by illness,
pulpits occupied by witless politicians salivating
for power. Here is a twang at the heart—for anyone
small enough to be born into this vast unwelcome.

Perhaps I, too, have never known real innocence at all.
I was too young to remember how the world looked
before the planes struck the first tower. But I know it
happened. This land does not let you forget what pain
it felt. Maybe my age of innocence was never innocent
at all, but even still, it was much closer, universes more
tender. Here is what I remember—we thought of life

as charming. We didn't spend all day searching for hope,
tapping fortified plastic touchscreens to same-day ship
it to our front doors. We went to school without masks
on, never felt our hearts drop at the mere sight of a bulky
trench coat. Here is a portrait of the world I knew—

I was happy. It wasn't perfect but I was happy enough
to believe it could be, and that it would be forever, that
place where people smiled, and held open doors, where
we weren't forced to make thirteen-year-old girls clutch
pepper spray on the way home from middle school. How
I thirst for their innocence the way I had it. I could walk

without looking over my shoulder. Breathe without the
possibility of quarantine. Love without fear that a law

could somehow make it illegal, that sanctions could be made overnight, under cover of darkness, a body being stolen and thrown into the river to drown, unnoticed.

Poor Connection

Twenty-first century lovesickness: I am tired
of only holding you through a pixelated screen.

It's supposed to be good enough. But I yearn
for conversations under crabapple trees, chapped
lip kisses, a love that is less hope and more touch.

Does anyone even remember how anymore?

Sweat and spit and strands of hair.
Limbs unfolding. The delicious sweetness of longing
for something ripe and flaming and palpable.

I know you and I do. We've crammed a whole
lifetime of it in a handful of short,
sweltering months.

For now,

it's video calls until the early hours,
my heart begging to leap through the glass.

Good enough to pass the days. But god,

how I dream of those trees.

Aren't All Hearts
Technically Failing?

All day long, I keep the door shut but the window open. Then I perform the rituals of a madwoman. They go like this: listen to podcasts about black holes (Spoiler alert: they're not actually holes! Quite the opposite actually. Look it up for your daily dose of useless wisdom) and systemic racism and the effects of anger on the heart. I'm worried about my heart. I've only lived twenty years but I'm still convinced it could be failing me. I mean, aren't all hearts technically failing, no matter how healthy they appear on an electrocardiogram? Any time I think about something remotely sad (black holes, systemic racism, the effects of anger on the heart), those dwellings manifest as a throbbing pain in the center of my ribcage, right where you'd aim to shoot me if you were, for some reason, trying to assassinate me. Or would it be considered murder instead? I didn't know the technicalities of vocabulary off the top of my head so I asked my good friend Google, who read me the definitions of those terms. Well, it turns out you have to be famous and important for your death to be considered an assassination, so I'd just be murdered, albeit in cold blood. That's bananas to me. It's the same damn thing. Still a bullet lodged in the bullseye of a human being. Still a pulsing life. Even the dignity of your death is defined by other people's perceptions of you. God, that's depressing.

Chest pain is always concerning. Whenever I feel that familiar fist clenching and unclenching in my core, my first reaction is to go, *Oh well. Goodbye Earth, I guess.* After that, the flood of possible realities drenches my mind. *Pulmonary stenosis. Mitral valve prolapse. Mitral regurgitation.* (Sounds sexy!) *Hypertrophic cardiomyopathy. Myocardial infarction. Ar-*

rhythmia. (Thanks again, Googs!) I memorized all of this medical jargon before I hit double digits because, for whatever reason, I was so stressed out in fifth grade that my pediatrician diagnosed me, with a sympathetic smile plastered on his face, with the condition of being smart enough to create my own suffering. Terminal illness, right? Nothing's actually wrong with my heart. My body is just a foolish narcissist.

[Side note: since all words are just *assignet* meaning, and there's no actual "love" in the word l-o-v-e, or m-a-n-i-c d-e-p-r-e-s-s-i-o-n in the body I inhabit, wouldn't *Arrhythmia* be a beautiful name for a baby girl if it meant something other than the meaning we gave it?]

Back to the rituals. After the slew of podcasts (because every recorded voice is insufferable after a few episodes), it's time for some light reading. Take today's selections, for example: an illegally downloaded PDF of Omi and Winant's racial formation theory. I read that until I was sufficiently over the human race. After that, fifty pages of *Normal People* by Sally Rooney, which has already introduced me to some delicious characters. And then after, my Facebook timeline. Incredible literature it is: a melting pot of awareness and ignorance and, of course, 45-year-old conspiracy theorists and front pew complainers. My favorite. And no, I'm not trying to insult your mother, or anyone's mother. I'm just talking, just like they do. People sure do have a lot to say about casserole recipes, Bible studies, and why we all should supposedly stop eating at Chinese restaurants in the age of… well, you know what they say.

The rest of the rituals are hardly rituals at all. I switch it up to keep it funky and fresh. Sometimes I Twitter-stalk literary agents who would never give my work a second glance, much less a first read. I'm not cool enough! I never have been. Other times I just sit here and wait for the mailman to come. Today he brought me pen pal letters from my three of my friends, Charli and José and Andy. That was one good thing, at least. I smiled while reading them, which, when I think about it now, is somewhat of a rarity these days.

These days, these days. Every day for the past four months I have met a novel variety of *angina*, which is fancy-talk for chest pain. It's different every time, the specific thing that tugs at my chest: black holes, systemic racism, the effects of anger on the heart, crippling writer's block, the fact that there's no cure to comorbid bipolar and borderline personality disorder, my shitty genetics, the American education system. This list is far from exhaustive.

But I'm trying to be less angry, less foam-at-the-mouth rageful, because one day my knack at inventing diseases might actually morph into a real disease, and I'd rather die of anything else (Meteorite! Poison! Lightning strike!) than *car◦io-anything*. I'd just hate to succumb to a predictable ending. A textbook finale of morphine and the intensive care unit of a hospital tucked away in the indifferent suburbs. I'd take assassination any day (Fine. *Mur◦er*.)

I wish Google had a direct answer for why I think these things, in this way, in this language. Like why I'm paralyzed by the inability to read others' perceptions of me, the madwoman in the stuffy bedroom. Why I'm obsessed with speaking in medical tongues and brainwashing myself into thinking I'm experiencing a massive cardiovascular event when I really just need to *Calm the Hell Down an◦ Stop Killing Myself Over Problems I Can't Solve.* Why I'm so eager to find the meaning of meaning itself (there is no real "meaning" in the word m-e-a-n-i-n-g) and why I can't leave middle-aged bigots alone. Google doesn't know why I am the way I am, no matter how many times I beseech her for answers. And that's okay. It's for my own good, I guess.

Yeah, there are still some things we're all better off not knowing.

Repent!

My friend swears *Apocalypse* is the wrong word.

I love the kid to death, but he's dead wrong.

I think we're all conditioned to associate *Apocalypse* and *Armage**on* and *Ju**gment Day* with falling buildings and city-hungry tsunamis and the Second Coming, sky opening up for the light to eat us whole. We revert to Revelation, the rapture, bridges collapsing atop fleeing families, and *Repent! The en* *is near!* The drama of the end days is a Hollywood box office spectacle and we romanticize it into our own collective prophecy. Pass the popcorn, please. You don't wanna miss the meteorite scene.

But I mean *Apocalypse* in the sense that all of our worlds have already ended. These are miserable hours. Touchless, reclusive, solitary hours. You don't have to be a Scripture fanatic to sense that this way of living hardly mirrors real life at all. I'm haunted by an ancient aftertaste, of pressing cheeks together in the summer like fleshy suction cups and being twirled to vertigo under Vincent's starry night. My *Apocalypse* looks like refreshing the news and forgetting to eat or water my plants. Like mourning over having experienced the tease of happiness. I felt it. I could touch it. But it was all an illusion.

It is easier to be a person around other people.

My *Apocalypse* is embarrassing. It's the stupid plight of a privileged twenty-something, childishly grieving the temporary end of her independence. It's thoroughly pathetic. Cabin fever and old traumas and reaching out to no one because it's too much trouble explaining to the world how you never truly know your loneliness intimately until you're a month into isolation and you realize you don't have anyone to miss. My apocalypse would warrant a 0% on Rotten Tomatoes.

It's that ba.

Not a single building has fallen. I'm writing to you from the stillness of my dollhouse life. Birds still chirp. It's April. My hair is getting long and I'm both crazy and stir-crazy.

And yet my friend still swears *Apocalypse* is the wrong word.

Leftover Soup, Bad Artist, and the Color Red

When you're stuck in the old there's nothing new to write about.
Same soup, just reheated. It's like trying to paint with a palette full of red.
Sure, you have scarlet, blood, rose, burgundy, and wine—which,
by the way, has even more varieties: merlot, sangria, cabernet.
At the end of the day, though, it's all just red. Red in different flavors,
saturations, intensities. You can't paint a world with just red.
Never mind, I lied. I'm sure someone can, but I've tried
and I've ruined far too many canvases trying to be bold, or feral,
like Rothko or Kandinsky. I can't do much with red.
I'm looking for a soft lavender, or an electric yellow,
or I'd even settle for a pink. Just anything new to dip my brush into,
a novel shade to fill my inkwell. These days, every poem I write
is a regurgitation of the last. Same concept,
different words to hold it captive.

Serve me something fresh on a platter, boil me a new kind of soup.
Italian wedding, French onion, a hearty clam chowder,
I hardly care at all. I want to burn my tongue with another broth,
cleanse my palate with a strange otherness. I'm drowning
in the alphabet with nothing left to spell. I could write about that,
but I already have. Here, I'll even do it again. 3, 2, 1—

I'd Say Their Names but There Are Far Too Many Now

I can't breathe, that's what he said with a knee against his neck.

And thousands of others like him have sung that three-word chorus, all of their gasping voices still echoing, still ignored as we turn a deaf ear and stare numbly, turning the street corner to avoid taking the side of the dying man.

Hatred is viral evil. A communicable disease spread in our streets, raised in our homes, still no known vaccine to stop its transmission. This morning I woke up to a world with my breath nowhere to be found. Land of the free, an illusion we were bred to believe, home of the…. *hurry!*

There's blood on the burning flag now. We wave it, we pledge allegiance—to bodies littering sidewalks, grocery store aisles boasting *buy one get one free!,* gas stations under the afternoon sun—black bodies, black lives, blackness an unforgivable sin.

They say *look the other way.* They say *they ʀeserveʀ it for resisting.* They say *it's not me, it's not someone I knew.* But complicity breeds more fathers wiped from history books. Privilege erases them as if they never existed. If you can still breathe easily in a world like this, then we do not occupy the same world.

I'd say their names but there are far too many now.

Pale Blue Fire

Carl Sagan once said, *In our obscurity, in all this vastness, there is no hint that help will come from elsewhere to save us from ourselves.*

We sent a rocket to space today with two fathers tucked away inside, on-lookers watching with heartbeats lodged in throats and eyes threatening rain. Brave hope, I call it, when the ship shuttles skyward. There is more to our world than the pain we inhabit. How we welcome the unknown, yet tethered to our soil are fathers dying. Tear gas and milk and piles of bodies lacerated by shards of glass. Tug-of-war for barricades, cars set aflame, rubber bullets lacing skin.

On this pale blue dot, pale blue fire. Everyone burns.

Yet still, the darker man dies.

Today one man's son watched his father's ship shatter the atmosphere. Another man's son watched his father die, battered and bleeding on the littered streets of a city that refuses to claim them.

Do you love us? Do you still care? I asked whatever benevolent force can still hear me. *Of course I still love you*, it replied.

It's the 30th of May in the year 2020 and love isn't enough anymore.

So Much of Absolutely Nothing

It's me
and this tragic blank page,
and our next-door neighbor wielding
some sort of deafening machinery to tidy up
the rose bushes that appear to have devoured even
their front door, and a half-full mug of unsweetened
Japanese green tea that has since given up its heat for the sake
of my disappointing writing, and the feeling of *Damn, so much
of absolutely nothing has happened this year,* and the page filling up
with lifeless, lackluster poetry every night. It's me and this vast
loneliness, me and touch-starvation, me and these incurable bouts of
missing you until I fall asleep, if I even do. It's me and forgetting
the involuntary reaction to human touch, that elbow-to-elbow
peace of a city crowd, of being a buoy in a sea of hot breath,
so much closeness and so little air to separate it. I hate that
I can't write or see you or lose myself in the world. Or
that I'm running low on vital hoping. For now, it's
me and the hatred of this calendar year, and how
the neighbor has stopped loudly grinding away
at the stubborn weeds that needed tending
to because at least, when he was, that
gave me something to listen to,
something small to believe in
for at least a few minutes.

Like It's Sunday Choir

I think I need to sing more.

The world's covered in sludge right now. Everyone's stepping on each other's toes, and that's not to say this wave of violence isn't for a good cause, because it is, and lately we have every reason to rage against. But I'm tired. I'm soaked in it. I'm sitting at my laptop contemplating the blunt inevitability of death, and how one day everyone I've ever accidentally crossed paths with at the grocery store self-checkout line and that one overcrowded undergraduate English class taught by a professor we all hated and every hand I've shyly grasped during a semi-romantic first date at the movies will one day return to dust for good. Every human body I've held close to mine. Thinking this way, it's nearly impossible to not fall straight into the empties. The existence of death makes life feel exhausting. We fall incurably in love and burn old bridges and wound others *for what?*

I need a way out of the clutches of death that isn't death itself. Like growing my own herbs. Or bird-watching. I get why this almost universally appeals to grandfathers and loners alike. I mean, it appeals to me now, too. Pastimes like that give you something to focus on while time brutally blurs the solid shapes of a life together. An anchor to hold onto while the colors run and bleed into each other, the landscape of your life beginning to come undone, unraveling right before your eyes as your bones begin to putrefy.

I think I need to sing more. I'm talking *sing* like it's Sunday choir and I'm six-and-a-half and missing my left front tooth and I believe in Our Savior Jesus Christ as my redeemer and the world has to know or nothing about me matters. Sing like tomorrow's the last day we'll have music, like we'll wake up and it'll be gone as if everything we hum under our breath never existed at all. Sing like I could lose function of my voice box and never sing again, because I actually could, which I guess, in its own right, is one kind of death.

I'm gonna sing like the world isn't losing its melody.

Like it's clean and it's calm and we can all still carry a tune.

State of the Union

Dictionary.com crowned "existential" Word Of The Year
for 2019. And how fitting she is for a world in flux.
We are still asking the age-old questions, these days
hardly expecting definitive answers. The Greeks
did it first. We simply have nothing original left to ask
in a macrocosm where nothing holds. Still we can't
seem to stop begging the sky for clarity, praying
for explanation like the farmland prays for rain.

This is our nature.
We are worn thin but this is our nature.

Is there such a thing as capital T Truth? Is love a real
breathing measurable entity or accidental chemistry?
Synapses fire, we can prove that, but not much else.
I'd tell you if I knew. But I don't. Neither do ancient texts,
dead philosophers, our mothers, or even Google.

Top trending searches in 2019: *What is Area 51?*
What is a VSCO girl? What is momo? What is
a boomer? What is qui● pro quo? What is
camp fashion? What is Disney Plus? What is
"Bir● Box" about? What is a Man●alorian?
What is Brexit? What is

the meaning of all of this? Will we ever know
the true satisfaction of knowing? All we have
in a cosmos without order is each other.

All we have is wonder. Wonder if these
breaths we pass between our bodies
amount to anything, or everything,
or nothing, at all.

I Will Not Give up on You, America

because I have seen the cool blue of your mountains
and heard the voices of your children rising to meet them.

It almost feels like enough

until I let the soles of my feet sink sufficiently into your soil
and feel myself become an intruder of a deeper, untold story.

Sometimes I swear I can still hear the dead scream
just standing there, listening to your heartbeat—

re, white, blue*—

The dead that built you. The dead you buried.

America, I want to believe in your goodness.

That you are still a breathing, wild thing,
that grace grows apart from your gardens and cities,
that there is more to you than just your wickedness.

Tell me the story.

Read to me so I can help you

rewrite it.

Blood on the Burning Flag

In order for poetry to mean anything in America it has to bleed.

No one wants to read the lamotrigine-fueled diaries of a privileged snob from her self-reported suburban inferno. No one wants to read about how *comparable* she feels to Sylvia Plath, at least in the sense of sharing "twin" emotional complexes. Or how *inspiring* she finds Renaissance philosophers with names as pretentious as their intellectual disciplines. And honestly I don't either. I can't even blame them.

There are better things to read about.

People want dignity! Blood on the burning flag! To earn your words by fighting for them makes a true American Hero. This is the Dream people die for—coming to life in these handwritten stories of survival scrawled in sweat. Work for the prize of being loved. Look death in the eyes and then write the hell about what it looked like. We all want to know. I mean, come on, don't you?

Poetry is becoming a competition in tragedy. Maybe it always has been. Maybe that's why we even bother to read it in the first place. At least that's why I do. To sink my teeth into something real.

War births beauty and I have nothing to offer but my dollhouse melo-drama. My piles of notebooks filled with *laven•er sky* and *faint music* and *first love* and *I never struggle•, at least not like them.* Nothing holds a candle to the piles of bodies memorialized on paper. The unburied dead, the poverty of a broken system. I call myself a poet for what I see. Yet I've seen nothing in comparison. Nothing.

That's the way it is and the way it should be. I won't play Devil's advocate. I'll never have the vocabulary to capture a struggle I've never known. It's not something you pick up and learn. This isn't Rosetta Stone. *I've never had to rage against.* I thank my lucky stars for that. I got damn lucky after all.

But I hope there's someone out there who still needs *lavender sky* and *faint music* and *first love.* And maybe even a little *I miss being seventeen* or *peach pits in the grass* or *I knew I'd love you eventually.* That maybe there's still some sort of market for that, someone who's tired of reading about the heroes some of us can never become.

Not all poets are heroes. Some of us are just poets.

And so we wave our white flags in surrender, still perfectly creased from the box they arrived in.

This World Isn't My Type Anymore

In my letters I write *Things have been goo♦! As goo♦ as they can be these ♦ays!*, forced reassurance leaking through black ballpoint ink, unpoetic lines smeared by a heavy hand. What I mean by *goo♦* is that I've got my hand stuck in a mixed bag. Some mornings I rise to an all-encompassing sense of dread, my body an anchor in a sea of boiling blood. Other mornings, though, I just make cinnamon oatmeal. Or a bagel with a thick layer of cream cheese. I'll put on the radio and lie in bed for an extra hour and not miss out on anything. At least I won't feel like I am. I've learned this life can feel sort of safe in the absence of the real thing. I'm not in love with it like I once was, no longer sucking the juice out of every short day I'm given, no longer chewing the rind for more. Content with what I can get—a hot shower, a vase of fresh flowers, an ounce of attention from the house cat—it's enough. I'm not rationing joy. I've just stopped chasing after it. I just let it chase me, let it serenade me, let it fall first.

Even If, Not When

this whole ordeal blows over, and the people are suddenly cured
of the fear that plagues them, rejoicing to the heavens *Amazing
grace, how sweet the soun♦ that save♦ a wretch like me,* I doubt
I'd be able to find the girl I lost in the golden days. Right now—

something inside of me hangs onto life by a fraying thread. I rot
within these walls, marking each hour by the tears I can still shed
to pass them, to make the minutes run with the wind I can't feel.

Morning, afternoon, night. Lather, rinse, repeat. There is no such
thing as grace in a body like mine, a vessel craving the soft touch of
real, breathing life, past the borders of pink-painted bedroom walls
and no appetite and lost sleep. I thirst for the life I lived before—

how I would sink my teeth into its sour rind and suck the juices out
and *run*, how I *RAN!* kicking up soil as I flailed myself in a thousand
directions at once, all of that mortal magic I felt back when I was still
invincible enough to seize the world with both hands, *ALLEGRO!*

I felt the wind in my hair and against my chest and on my bare
knees bloodstained and kissed by grass and I believed, truly

believed *grace* to be interchangeable with *bo♦y*

which was synonymous with freedom and timelessness
and the electricity of being young and still unstolen from

I ONCE WAS LOST, BUT NOW AM FOUND

were the words I would scream all the way back home, burning.

Privilege for the Privileged

It's nearing the end of the longest March we've ever known and nothing feels real and I can't get off my phone because somehow it's permanently attached to my palm. I've stopped trying to shake it off. All day long I contemplate the idea of regression and how I've never in my life felt less human and more like some extinct primate further up on our cursed family tree. But I am human, and if you're reading this you (most likely) are, too, which is an inescapable and horribly tragic fact of which we've been made painfully aware, at least more so, recently. I know this because I can't stop watching gory video footage and news reports featuring other humans in makeshift ICU wards in various corners of the earth, how this thing we're all afraid of doesn't give a damn if you're an old man in some European city with a juicy life tucked under his belt or a fifth-grade kid with purple braces and freckled cheeks. It doesn't give a damn if we're afraid, either. We're running out of hospital beds and respirators and doctors and time. The whole world is flatlining. But time, what a foolish, fickle construct, how we're always running from here to there in our fanciest shoes and fakest egos trying to fill our pockets with shiny, worthless things. *Time is privilege for the privileged.* I know this because I see it, every single day, in the mirror when I stare at my bumbling hypocrisy and my perfect health and my working lungs and the fact that I am in the prime of my life and yet I choose to spend time watching people suffocate in bubble helmets. Their families won't even be allowed to bury them and yet I have the gross audacity to watch in silence, safely tucked under the covers of a false sense of security, repeating, *Well, I'm glad it's not me.*

If Dickinson Was Right and Hope Is, in Fact, the Thing With Feathers

It goes like this.

Wake up, fall into the abyss of timeline updates, scroll through the carnage I slept through. New day, new wrath. I grow more weary of the world every day I am forced to wake up in it. Tell me, where is the world we remember?

I am weary of those who have a voice but do not speak. I am weary of those who claim their rights have been stolen from their hands when all that is asked of them is patience. *The worl· will open again,* that is a promise. *But now! Now!* they won't be commanded to wait. I wish I could give them grace.

I used to write letters to my children. Addressed each of them by name, signed them *Mom*, wrote of how proud I am of the faces I do not know yet. There's one for when my daughter turns sixteen, when she's twirling in a silver dress with her eyes lined and hair curled. And another for my son to open in his college dorm room the night we leave him for the next chapter. But it feels wrong now, to bring innocence into a world tainted by this much blood. I do not know whether to hold onto those envelopes, to safe-keep them under layers of dust, or to tuck them into a glass bottle, say goodbye, and let the river do what it will.

It goes like this.

One day you're young and you dream of your own family and you're going to name your daughter Ava and teach her how to be happy since nobody taught you. You're naive and you're sparkling and the world still feels good *enough*, not perfect, but still a world in which you wouldn't mind one day having a handful of laughing angels sprinting around the kitchen island, their laughter spilling everywhere. One day you still keep a broken-winged bird fluttering in the cavern of your ribcage, a fledgling thing called *Hope,* until you wake up to another day, realize that nothing flutters inside of you anymore, and when you breathe out to ask *Why?* the room fills with feathers.

There Were Good Things, Too

Like that one time my friends and I ordered a pepperoni pizza so grotesquely large it couldn't fit through the apartment door horizontally and how the slices were bigger than two of our heads stacked on top of each other. I have found that there are perks to the apocalypse and sometimes they look like greasy paper towels and football on TV featuring the eeriness of empty stadiums and lack of belligerent cheering that makes normal feel *normal*. We're accidental artists of making the most out of living, even when it's been seven months of isolation and bad news and unexpected obituaries, when all of California is on fire, when our streets are stained with blood, when *right* and *wrong* have blended together until the definitions eventually became horrifyingly interchangeable, when it feels as if the timeline itself has torn at its seams, spilling the guts of humanity onto the fabric of the universe and staining it, when it's another morning in a broken simulation and it's far too easy to believe in the cruelty of this world. I want to remember that there were good things, too. Like how we were all here together, feeling the weight of it all on a Friday evening, haunted by old dreams, how we collectively decided, *Hell to it all, why don't we just order a pizza?*

I'll Take That

Safe things—Mitski on my record player, my mother's thin fingers
French braiding my hair, bananas that are just ripe enough—I hold
onto these safe things as I let my life unravel in my hands. Today
I feel a little bit better than yesterday. *I'll take that,* I tell the sky,
as I remind my body to inhale without thinking too deeply about
how. I'm tired of thinking about illness and death and why my chest
hurts all the time. I'm sick of making myself sick. And so I clutch
these harmless, healthy things with every gram of strength I have.
Outside my house right now, someone is shooting a gun. Ever so
often, my mother and I jump. But it's nothing, it's nothing, and
she finishes the braid and we're humming, we're humming, and
I'm still alive in a room that loves me, and no part of me is dead.

Today, After Too Many Consecutive Ones Spent Panicking

I did not panic.

Instead, I caught the bus without crying and texted my mom that I didn't.

Nor did I think much about death or check my pulse fifty times to make sure it hadn't found me yet.

Instead, I made myself a sunflower butter and blueberry jam sandwich and ate every bite of it on a park bench, crusts included, without letting the morsels of guilt get stuck in my teeth or in my throat.

I did not panic.

Today is the first day of September and you drove me to the drugstore in the rain to pick up my new prescriptions. On the way there we sang along to cheesy country songs written about the pandemic.

I did not think much about the pandemic.

Later, after binging *How I Met Your Mother* like we always do, we talked about the future over death-by-chocolate ice cream. A year from now who knows where we'll be.

I did not panic.

Instead, I held you close and told you I loved you

and did not think about how long I'd be able to—

I just did.

When My Kids Ask Me Why I Write

Well, I'll tell them,

sometimes you wake up and twist your ankle on the way downstairs
before a very important meeting, and later you find out it is shattered
in four different places, and even though you have big things to do
you must sit very still and wait for them to fuse again. Sometimes

you wake up and it's pouring rain so you make a pot of bold coffee
and read the news and it's just as depressing as yesterday's headlines
and so you decide to do something mindless like fold clean laundry
into categorized piles and then the phone rings and you find out

that someone you love has died, and so you stop folding clothes
and start shaking like a stilt house in a hurricane, and you forget
about the laundry and the coffee and the rain, and so you write.

Sometimes waiting isn't fair, I'll tell them. And sometimes
you must put the world on pause, turn off the television,
and let whatever is broken heal over, bones hardening until
you are whole enough to move. That's why I write, dear child,

because sometimes people die and the interstates are flooded
and another church was bombed in a city you can't pronounce

but you have a pen and a mind and a heart that can't stop bleeding.

Why do I write? Because what else would I do with all of this waiting?

I Talk to No One Else

Listless and unromantic, I wallow
to the skipping of rain on my roof.
Bedroom walls make alright lovers
when no one else is around to fill
these echoing caverns of silence.
I'm tire•, I whisper to nothing,
an• not in the way you think.
Tired like it's the wet season
in my hometown, and I miss
your baby hairs and peach fuzz
and the whole anatomy of you,
more *there* than my own skin.

Dearest Season We've All Been Waiting For

We wish for grass-stained kneecaps and sudden summer downpours puddling around muddy bare feet and strollers carrying babies that babble and wave their dimpled hands as if they've met us in another life. We wish for yard sales run by someone's grandparents packed with useless collectibles from a war we weren't alive for and sprawling picnics that leave our fingers stained cherry red, tying stems with our tongues like we're sixteen and curious if we'd be good at making out with our high school crushes. We wish for so much, dear summer. The juice of ripe pomegranates dripping down our palms and over-chlorinated swimming pools and pitiful attempts to suntan. We've had a darn hard spring, summer, so we place our trust in you.

We wish for bomb pops from sketchy ice cream trucks driven by oddball characters we distrust and Independence Day sparklers purchased in bulk from the corner firecracker stand even though patriotism is becoming a dead language, and rightfully so. We wish for the baptismal cool of mountain lakes and the intoxicating fury of ocean waves when we pinch our noses and go under. We wish for an end to hospitals packed with undeserving souls and the hatred that permeates our people. Heal us, summer. Go easy.

Because we're overdue with wishes and we're spilling over.

Freshly squeezed farmers market blood orange lemonade.

Vinyl records that skip through open windows.

Less blood and more mercy.

Love always,

All of us.

As It May Be

Maybe we'll bring disco back. Or, at the very least, ironic disco, because we all know our attempts to resurrect the '70s would make a mockery out of a cultural revolution. Maybe we'll go outside more. Hike the waterfalls we kept procrastinating, kiss in the woods like suburban teenagers desperate for any variety of escape, sleep under the stars in too-small tents. We'll make public displays of affection in vogue again. We'll start dancing with our hair down, *really* dancing, like it's 1969 and we are the counterculture generation, so intertwined we appear to be one breathing body. Maybe we'll learn to hug our loved ones goodbye: before catching that red-eye flight, in the aftermath of heated arguments, when they leave for work in the morning, every morning. No excuses, no forgetting, none of it for granted.

Privilege

A year from now we'll be wiser because of this.
We'll have melted back into our original molds:
high fives and cheek kisses and shared milkshake
straws. It'll be a springtime tailor-made for loving,
weaving dandelion stems together, fashioning crowns
to place around the heads of those we hold tender.

I'll squeeze your hand a little tighter, call the act of
doing so *privilege,* complete and total *privilege*—
for *to have* is one thing but *to hol* is another, how
the latter can too easily crumble under the weight
of fear. We watched it happen. We were stolen from.

A year from now we'll remember those strange days
of forbidden *han**-in-han**,* that time we kept flowers
rooted in the soil because there were no crowns to make
that season, as if springtime never came at all. *Privilege,*
we'll say, all of this beauty *privilege,* for there was a time we
almost lost it, but here it is, a world *to hol**,* and each other.

There Will Be More

long walks home, more *Come on Eileen* on loop
blaring through sunroofs open wide, more plum
lipstick staining the Adam's apples of the boys
we love, more *you hang up first, I •i• last night,*
more sneaking one last kiss before the door shuts,
more cruising through the rich neighborhoods,
Christmas Eve, imagining their lofty electric bills
while Sinatra blankets the air as purely as the snow
we scarcely get around here, more pressing palms
together, finding where our heart lines intersect,
where our life lines end, more saving pictures of
dream dresses for our weddings still many years
away, more learning that sometimes the only real
prayer we have is blind hope, skeletons of faith,
clinging to the promise that *there will be more,*
there has to be, we have to get home somehow.

Highs and Lows

I can't bear it so I say *I'll see you soon.*
It's far more comforting than *I ιon't*
know when or *however long this takes*
to pass. I ache for our days in the sun:

faint light streaming through curtains
of better days, not days like these, how
we sulk around our homes fearing what
sickness might be carried by wind, what
might become of these uncharted hours.

I yearn for the softness of anything easy.
Sunday mornings, pancake batter, your
thin index finger tracing every low valley
my knuckles form. Pretty privileges: all

of this delight I took for granted. Maybe
I would've held onto you a little longer
if only I knew the kind of fear we'd face.

I'll see you soon.

Measure the time in Sundays. In breakfasts.
In the peaks and mountains my knuckles
make, squeezing your palm, *however long*
this takes, to stop the sun from sinking.

This World Gazes Back

Sometimes helicopters fall with fathers and daughters still inside of them. And at the same time there's some sort of virus hanging in the air making fear point its ugly finger. Who is responsible for this? What wretched nation, what sick corner of the world? There must be someone tampering with the wires. And while we're at it, what sort of madness causes a continent to burn itself dry? It doesn't just happen. Something always instigates. We mumble words like *power* and *influence* and *annihilate the enemy* the same way trembling mothers mumble desperate prayers under war-torn skies. A child who has never known love considers the trajectory of something illegal hidden under an overcoat. No one yet knows how many hearts he'll break today. Down the street a young ballerina refuses dinner for the fourth time this week to feel pretty under stage lights. She imagines how beautifully she'll glow tomorrow by turning down another slice of fruit tonight. And somewhere in a city I've never been, someone called Dad stands with sunken shoulders at the cash register of truth. His pockets are empty. Tonight the children will feast on hope alone. Still, none of them will ever see him cry.

Who is responsible for this? Could it be fate? Reason?

For my own sanity I choose to believe it is not all tragedy. There is still the inevitability of springtime in world as broken as ours. Someone will spare bread to the children, those rail-thin dreamers raised on street wishes. Someone standing with one foot already off the bridge begging destiny for a sign—just one—will see it, from the opposite side of the bay, some sort of green-light savior. A bird taking flight. A vision of Jesus. A memory of a first love. They will inhale the stuff of life and swing their shaking knees back over the safety rail. Life will continue, just like that.

Just like morning comes. Just like night falls. There will always be someone, hunched over while the world sleeps peacefully, untangling the wires.

And War Might Be Raging Somewhere

but today there will be weddings and robins resting in bird baths
and toothless drooling babies and mothers who rise early to make
sandwiches with the perfect peanut-butter-to-grape-jelly ratio
and giddy teenage girls trying on lavender homecoming dresses
and fat house cats that sleep through the afternoon and children
laughing—children are always laughing—in classrooms and meadows
and decrepit alleyways as missiles soar just blocks away. and today
might be the last for many, but for the peach fuzz jaundiced newborn
breathing air for the first time, it is still opening day in a world
that is still good, still patiently waiting, in spite of it all.

V

SELF AS WAR

Hibiscus

The mind is most honest when the stars are out.
There are no pretenses. There are no hideaways.
After midnight, I lie awake and dream of things
too shy for daytime. Things that go unspoken,
like how the pink hibiscus flowers on the shirt
he wore when he took what was not his, what
I never asked for, what I never gave him, those
flowers still bloom on the backs of my eyelids
when I try to sleep. Bloody petals, split stems,
no matter the season they are always there, like
weeds that return even after pulling, even after
all evidence has been erased, the roots devoured
by solid earth, they still grow without mercy.
The mind is most honest when the stars are out.
And I see him now, in the act of taking, cotton
and sweat, my voice begging him *no*, and hibiscus.

Facedown in the Grass

I am sick, Mom.

I am so sick that I convinced myself
I'd been reincarnated as a glass sculpture,
abstract and unmoving, against the pale blue
hydrangeas at the butterfly gardens today.

I am too sick for the gardens, Mom.

You took me there to forget myself, I know,
to feel—for a fleeting moment—less *hostage*
of my min• and more •*ragonfly surfing*
the lilypon•. But nothing ever becomes
of your worthy endeavors and I am fated
to be the dead among the living, the girl lying
facedown in the grass, praying for the grave.

Take me home, Mom.

I am sorry that I cannot grow,
that I am not a wild, blooming thing
capable of being swayed by summer air
and wanting nothing more than to live.

Mine are the roots that cannot clutch, Mom—
and maybe I am far too sick to stay.

I Said No

It's not about the act itself but the aftermath. After it happened I couldn't pass by a mirror for months without resurrecting the image of hand-prints on hips, the kind that didn't scrub off in the shower no matter how hard I tried, burning my bones, the memory of bruises reddening my ribs. I remember slinking back into my father's sweatshirt and leaving in the morning like nothing happened. You were fast asleep and I didn't wake you—just slipped on yesterday's wrinkled clothes, ran my hands through the knots in my hair you made when I was too dizzy to tell you to stop, and put last night's unfinished homework, stained amber by your cheap liquor, back into my school backpack, unfeeling. And then I didn't feel anything for the rest of the year. But after I left your dorm room that morning I got coffee. Two cups of half-and-half coffee creamer into a medium-sized styrofoam cup of dark roast. I took the window desk on the third floor of the library and wrote a mediocre essay on the Dark Lady in Shakespeare's Sonnet 130 through a post-structuralist lens. At the campus ice cream shop that night, over double scoops of mint chocolate chip in a waffle cone, a close girlfriend of mine asked me what was new in my world, and I said, *Nothing much, just looking forwar* to Thanksgiving break,* and adjusted the collar of my shirt so she wouldn't see what you did. That was the beginning of my fear of love. It's not about the act itself but the aftermath. The cavernous space between the me I knew and the me that couldn't be touched without the compulsion to scream. If anyone asked about you then I would've lied through my teeth and said some-thing along the lines of *We're goo*. We're not together anymore but we're goo*.* I wouldn't have told them about the way you made me swallow a pill *just in case, I *on't know, just *o it.* I wouldn't have told them about crossing paths with you later that week, that all-knowing smirk plastered on your face, and how seriously I contemplated the height of a rooftop and whether or not it could eradicate my suffering. It's not about the act itself but the aftermath. It was the way I kept going, pretending we were still best friends, that the night never happened, that we just fell asleep and nothing more, and you took nothing.

Everyone has their own share of myths.

This is the one I've been telling. Until now.

Truce

Staredown between the neon orange bottle
and my hand already cupped in anticipation.

This unfolding drama is what I do not tell you.
The story goes like this: *I almost do and then*

I don't. Count to ten. Thing of the good things,
like mother taught you when you were young

and yet sad enough to die. I've been rehearsing
the good things for decades. Orange marmalade

and rich people's lawns that water themselves,
my records from the '70s and the sepia freckles

that scatter across the nose of the man I love.
I'll stay for that, I guess, and the staredown ends.

September, in My Head

will always bring back visions of my body, nearly nineteen,
crumpled like an old shirt in the corner of a dorm room
belonging to a boy I thought loved me. Poor girl, if only
I could scoop her up from the cold tile and feed her bowls
of her mother's homemade chicken noodle soup, if I could
finger the coarse knots from her unwashed hair, if I could
tell her to run from anyone who tries to claim her skin
as their own. September, in my head, is a kind of winter
nothing ever prepares me for, no matter how many pass
before my eyes. Every September, I am eighteen again,
and I'm waiting for him to stop laughing at how small
I feel, weeping hard into purple knees and wondering
what else I must give up to deserve a kiss goodnight.

An Anti-Love Letter to the Flutter in My Chest

or, in other wor♦s, the anxiety that plagues me

I have been trying to find the root of your obsession with me. You are far worse than the worst lover I've ever had, you know—the one who kept writing me love poems a whole year after I stopped reading them, the one who would stand in front of my bedroom window at night marveling at my lack of awareness through the curtains. I wake each morning and there you are again, singing songs about death in my ear, convincing me it is creeping closer. *To♦ay?* you breathe against my neck, *It might be your last one, ever.* All day I feel the stickiness of your seduction, cold beads collecting on my forehead. I check my pulse at least a hundred times before noon, anticipating the rises and falls, panicking over a sudden skip. It's just how I live now, constantly in search of the possible ways I could die without warning. Everything is a threat. Even the yellow wildflowers growing along the perimeter of my apartment are loaded guns. Too bright, too intimidating, too showy. Grocery store aisles are coffins. When my love asks me if we should buy pancake mix for Sunday morning breakfast, I do not see him nor the box he holds in his hands. All I can see are the vague outlines of a life I can only be part of through the curtains.

When I Try to Imagine the Woman for Whom You'd Leave Me

there are no pills in sight, no crumpled just-in-case goodbye letters,
no clumps of hair on her desk from far too much worrying for you.

Her friends (and she has them) would describe her as *bubbly* or *bright*
but certainly not *difficult* or *temperamental* (it's fine; I've made peace).

She can design a mean bouquet. She has a signature dish. She could
even be a model, though her humility prevents this. She has the frame

for it. If she writes poetry (though unlikely) she'd never write a poem
titled "When I try to imagine the woman for whom you'd leave me."

She sticks to nature. Childhood. The simplicity of her love for you.
She's a damn good writer and she doesn't need an ounce of trauma

to write things you'd read. In my head, I see green eyes and fair skin
and confidence that never borders on cocky. But I do not see sadness.

I do not see the variety that my body, awkward and uncouth, emits.
I could recognize it anywhere. But not in her, your Aphrodite, holy

human cathedral. She talks about the past. She has no mean streak.
Even I would pray to her. I would consecrate myself at her shrine

for having everything I cannot call my own. When I try to imagine
the woman for whom you'd leave me I see someone even I would

accidentally love. Her easy poetry and femininity and lack of grief.
Her way with flowers and food and loving you without killing you.

Someone Better

Mom,

One day I'll be happy enough
to not cry on your birthday.
I won't have to beat my fists against
the slope of my skull
or purple my thighs over the unfair ordeal
of having a brain like mine. I wish
I could be an easy daughter, that I could
find you a better one on the highest shelf
of a seaside gift shop and swaddle her
in wrapping paper to place in your hands,

someone better

who won't hate the body you gave her
the kind of someone you deserve

but never got.

Eden, Aflame

a privilege it would be
to be a little less fire.

less microcosm of chaos. less coming apart at the seams.
less doubled-over Holy Lance, millennia still bleeding.
less scarlet fever soul. less gunfire.
less gaping mouth, letter O, still sounding.

to be, instead,
more pastoral meadow. more cherub on cathedral ceiling.
more first real love, years still sweet, still sore.
more sleeping baby. more sky before snow.
more mother's touch. more Sunday morning, still quiet.

the definition of Paradise is this
and it is lost to me.

I fear I have fallen from the grace of myself.

A Letter to Anxiety

No one touches me quite like you.

Sweet-talking flirt, you have mastered of the art of *taking*,
harvesting words straight from my throat to take home,
to call your own, to hang like plastic letter magnets
on the refrigerator door.

Sometimes I worry you are the only love of my life.

But what kind of poem can you write with a stolen alphabet,
you cruel surgeon? Sometimes I try to speak
and nothing comes out.

And do you know how terrifying it is to stand
with mouth agape, paralyzed with no sound?

It's *The Scream* that never ends.

I know that lovers come and lovers go.

I know it well.

You stay, though.

You always stay.

Double-Edged Swords

Everyone I love leaves!

Everyone I love leaves!

Everyone I love leaves!

It's a song I can't stop singing, a Bible verse of my own I can't stop believing in. I am scared of love and all it entails, scared that, written in my marrow exists an ultimatum, *Everyone you love will leave you!* I am scared of the way you clutch me unconditionally because all I have grown to know is condition after condition after condition. How do you take a wrecking ball to these walls without striking yourself down in the process of doing so? How do you demolish the idea without leaving the idea of yourself in ruins? The art of mutual exclusivity. I can't keep breathing this air but without it I would die. Unfair laws of the universe, you govern me and all of my weakness.

I am scared of how much I love you. I am scared of your feet. I don't know how fast they are capable of running away from me, from us, from everything we are currently building. I am scared of your smile, crooked and genuine, because of how beautiful it is. I've never seen beauty of that calibre. I don't know what to do with it. I don't know how to not stare, dumb and out of words. No language. No way to express how utterly bone-chilling you are, the audacity of your beauty—a fist formed to all the ugly in the world. You are remedy to the unbecoming. You are grace in a graceless world.

I am scared of how much I hunger for the end. Or not even the end, but a way to stop feeling the particular sensation of tragedy that consumes me upon rising each morning, a method of anesthetizing the perpetual throb of my body, a tangle of nerves and pressure points—how to numb the lack of control.

Sometimes I speak and am surprised at the sweetness of my own voice. I feel bitter, conniving, burning, and rotten. But when I catch myself talking I am stunned at how good I am a concealer of pain, how you can hear music resounding where my pain would otherwise echo. I mask the ache with honey, fresh petals, warm tea. You'd never guess that beneath the pleasant exterior I am an infernal scream. I am something begging to be torn, put down, ended. I am plaster and drywall covered in dainty pink wallpaper. Tear me down, break me, leave me in my own wreckage I am begging you. But then again, I don't know if you could handle it—seeing me all mangled like that, too far gone to cry for help, nothing but a heap of broken promises, a deconstructed fortress.

I shuttle so quickly between too much and not enough. As if I am constantly suspended inside the webbing between both. The lacking side of me thirsts for adventure, for miles of European countryside and enough time to disappear in it. This side wants plane rides and exotic cuisine, poetry and color. But my other side, my incoherent, overwhelmed half, wants nothing more than to forget it all, to abandon all of this *wanting more* and never quite reaching the precipice of satisfaction. That side wants stillness, dreams of growing roots for stability, hungers for the pleasure of staying put.

I really did fall in love with a war. I guess I just underestimated how much I would want it to end.

Invisible Movements

I do not like the motion my mind makes
tossing and turning with the bold inertia
of a spinning coin. I long to live as still
as a man-made marina. As a scaffolded
cathedral, no one to hear its song. To be
that free, no known vernacular, rooted
without expectation. Sacred unmoving.
Have you ever yearned to be a fortress?
Unpolluted meadow, virgin dusting of
first snow. *I am you, I am you, I am you.*

Prison Road

Don't be too hard on yourself.
I hate seeing you miserable.

You see, I can't.
It's part of what makes me a writer.
Each sentence must bleed,
steak knife thrust in a human heart.
Poetry without passion is just symbolic
nonsense, words on paper signifying
nothing, eating space, *u s e l e s s.*

It is the primal urge of the poet
to tear each line to shreds,
bare-handed shrieking
I AM DONE WITH POETRY
slamming the book shut
but never *really* being *one*
with poetry, because poetry
is a door bolted shut. Is
a maximum security prison.
Is also an open road.
Once you're there you're there,
but also you're there forever.

Get used to the misery, sweet inventor.
If you finish without your own blood
on your hands, you aren't finished at all.

Without Your Name, Who Are You?

I still don't know. I wish I had words for this strange curse:
the way I accidentally leave hearts gasping for oxygen
like pathetic fish out of water, how I cannot move
but an inch without burning someone, something.
I am comprised of far too much intensity. If my body had
a list of ingredients, it would read *fire, inferno, conflagration,*
the label burned at the edges, the fine print charred black as night.

How strange—I'm a water sign. Yet so much of me incinerates.
Fire is familiar. Fire is home to me. I am safe among embers.

This I know because my poetry bleeds like a glass of wine
knocked into the lap of a white dress. And my heart, too,
bleeds like a sunset spilling into the ocean: no boundaries,
no laws enforced or governed, an open wound you can't stop staring at.

I am both the abandonment and the abandoned,
both the water and the fish, both the sea of flames
and the body at the stake, burning, burning, burned.

And I'll love you just like that, too, scarlet tragedy.
A pretty, giggling, mesmerizing nightmare,
writing you into poetry that melts holes in your hands.

Eighteen Years

My eighteenth birthday was spent crying on the shore of a frozen beach.
It was all I requested: poetry books and a weekend with the ocean.
My parents and I wore parkas in mid-November,
the frigid breath of late autumn blowing wet sand into our faces.
That night, I bundled up on the balcony, drunk on sparkling cider
and the tragedy of being me.
The loneliness of finally being old enough
to understand that the ocean cannot cure every sickness.
That only time can heal open wounds, and that
saltwater can only do so much to stop the infection.
Sand cannot desensitize the bite of heartache,
the nostalgic pang of birthdays past–
a time of candles dripping wax,
and when blowing them out
(*Happy birthday to you,*
happy birthday to you,
happy birthday dear–)
didn't feel so hollow.

I have forgotten what I wished for.
Maybe a sailboat, maybe a car ride home,
maybe a sunrise that didn't sting.

Thought as Shape

I am trying
not to think of
myself as tragedy
or even really at all.
I don't want to think.
Not of April and not of
being 17 or 18 or 19 or
being stupid crazy in love or
free-falling out of it or about
what tomorrow will bring or all
the places I've ever called home or
having friends or losing them or my
perpetually unkempt hair or the one freckle
on your neck I touch when I'm lying on your chest
or the way you sing to yourself and call yourself a fool
even though we both know I am a fool for you and proud of it.
I am trying so hard not to think of how my life lately has
been feeling like running in circles with untied shoes
tripping over concrete skinning both of my knees
and hiding them under my jeans so no one finds
out I've been hurt so I can just keep running.
I am trying not to think of myself as evil
for having a heart that loves so loudly
the way it screams always waking up
the entire neighborhood. I don't
want to think. I want to return
to when it was easy to rest
and think about April

and 17 and 18 and
being so in love I
truly believed
there was no
way I could
fall out
of it.

I Don't Know What You're Scared Of

but for me, it's formal dining rooms and how to eat neatly in them
and family portraits with everyone clad in the same shade of beige
and how unlike your mom is from my mom and how unlike you
are from me, even though I hunger for you and would like to sit
with you in the car with your brothers while you talk about what
I don't understand, like football and Catholic school and loving
your hometown even after leaving it. I want to tell you the reason
why these things scare me but I'm too invested in the pearliness
of your skin, yet another region of unlikeness, and the strange way
I touch you and feel ivory and snowfall and Jesus and America
and everything I wanted to be when I was younger and obsessed
with purity, whiteness, the privilege I could taste on my first love's
lips, later stuck in my teeth, then in my throat. I'm not scared
of you, not at all, but the way I choke back my first language
when I shake hands with the world that will never welcome it.

Origami Heart

My first smile made its grand debut
at seven this evening. It only took
my mother's hand squeezing mine
and my father returning from the
grocery with a bouquet of yellow
sunflowers. I have sobbed my way
through this day for no real reason
other than my own fear of nothing.
I have convinced myself I am folding
inward, that my body has reached
its final hour, that I will buckle
until I am spent. This is no poem.
This is the heart of a sick girl,
nauseated and sinking in horror.

Loose Tapestry

I play wallflower to your world.

Your life—crisply folded, deliciously cookie-cutter,

coordinated family photos that take hours to stage.

I will never relate to your relations.

Mine—we're a loose tapestry,

more rough-and-tumble, less methodical.

Do not misunderstand me, love—

I envy the order of your universe, but mine

has no formal design or blueprint to follow.

I've never had to pose before, angling my shoulders

to please the blinding flash.

Forgive my awkward stance, my lack of grace.

It's evident I come from somewhere else.

A place where posture doesn't matter, where Dad

comes from around the corner without warning

to snap photos of us laughing over our breakfast plates,

never stopping to count down from three but that's okay

because in that world at least I do not wonder if my smile

looks forced in the Christmas card you'll never send.

All Artists Have to Suffer
for Their Art

I blame my bad poetry on good medication. You win some, you lose
some, I guess. When it's three o'clock in the morning and I'm clawing at
my skin trying to flee the cage of my body, I bleed out Pulitzer Prize-win-
ning work. It's like I rely on psychosis for the right words. But when I'm
sitting pretty, brain numbed to a satisfactory stillness, and I've tossed back
the powdery pills that make the scary thoughts dissolve like granulated
sugar on the tongue, I'm suddenly at a standstill with the keyboard. This
is a cold war of my own invention, but this time it's just me against me. I
can't move a finger when I'm stable, when I'm smiling, when I'm not ac-
tively dangling one foot over the edge, threatening to shift my center of
gravity.

All artists have to suffer for their art, I pretentiously announced to my English class at seventeen. I had convinced myself that I was a someday vi-
sionary, a *literary proigy aheas of her time!* But in retrospect, that was
probably just undiagnosed bipolar disorder already in full swing, invading
the nooks and crannies of a muddled mind. Nevertheless, I was writing
back then—a lot and well. I won awards. I touched people enough to
make them weep. I decorated my bookshelves with gold medals and crisp
certificates and gazed at them all day as a means of inspiration. But I was
also dangerously sick. I'd skip dinner and break skin and pen goodbye letters to my friends and almost send them, but at least I was writing, right?

Sometimes I Hate Poetry

because it feels like pulling invisible threads
through clogged pores or dry heaving foreign
objects of nothingness lodged somewhere
between the throat and chest cavity. I hate
poetry occasionally for the way it leaves my
ego wrung dry and desperate and my frame
brittle and these red eyes glazed over entirely
as if they have seen too much to hold any of it.
There are days when excavating the mind for
the most worthy words feels like an errand left
to run or another heart left to break reluctantly
and be done with forever, killing something real.

I' like to write about flowers tonight or how
we witnesse the first real sunset all winter
*through the blin*s of your apartment kitchen
or how I hate everything about the past few years
except meeting you an loving you an* keeping
you. Or maybe something about how I miss home
*but *on't at the same time because everything there
*remin*s me of everything I've lost an* being there
makes me pray I coul give up my history, but I can't,
*because *oing so woul* mean killing something real.*

Nights like tonight everything I write feels pitiful,
like crying at the dentist or not knowing what to say
when someone new asks me where I'm from. I hate

poetry some days because no matter how hard I try
to pull those invisible threads through my skin once
and for all, I lose grip. They slip back in, pointless
to the point of no return, objects of nothingness.

Holy Fantasies

On bad days I like to pretend the universe knows me.

That she's memorized the way I pick at my split ends,
how my left eye's only lazy in photos, how I grew up
dreaming of one day becoming the patron saint of
something wild. Like bad poetry or bipolar disorder
or far too much passion to fit inside a five-foot-five
frame. Imagine that—being martyred for a cause
worth dying for. Even now I'd still die for emotion.

I fantasize over the stars knowing the things I hold
secret to my soul, of the moon looking back at me
in complete understanding. All of these celestial
bodies daring to acknowledge my own, choosing
to find the horror film starlet crying on the floor
of the shower, mourning the loss of belief. I am
no saint. I like to imagine the universe seeing this—
that she could recognize the expression on my face.

I like to pretend she's been observing me for twenty
years. That she saw the flicker in my eye when I was
born and knew that I'd be the patron saint of trying.

Holy fantasies, how you consume me. The cosmos
could not be more indifferent, yet the dream rages on.

Objections

When I was younger and blinded by the spell of perfection, I wanted nothing more than to settle down, to let the dust of existence bury me in a world of plastic. I wanted to be like those silly wedding cake figurines: my Ken doll dream man and me, perfectly balanced on the top tier of everything safe, our feet plastered securely into frosting. *I •o, I •o, I •o.* I craved stability, *until •eath •o us part*: a handful of bright-eyed children as proof of success, a man strong enough to keep me on my feet, a white picket fence surrounding it. I wanted Sunday mornings and rolling hills, to be a mother, to be content.

But somewhere along the way I found myself entranced by the open gate, the road that leads somewhere new. I want to eat the cake with my bare hands now, letting Mr. and Mrs. Something fall from their pompous pedestal, the suicide of artificial bodies. I want someone who will starve with me instead. To shove it all in my mouth in sloppy handfuls, no time to nibble gracefully around silver cutlery. I dream now—of the rush of inconstancy, of chasing the lust of impulse, of spontaneous combustion. I want Saturday nights and lost voices, to be a wild soul running in the night, to be forever hungry for more cake.

I •o, I •o, I •o.
Watch me.
I'll marry that open gate,
and for the vows
I'll walk right through.

Unsolved Mystery

A switch flipped and part of me died.

The part in question—unknown to me.
This death did not leave behind a body.

Or a shadow. Or a silhouette in the grass.

I am trying to find the missing piece again,
fingers fumbling for a switch on the walls
of every place I've ever called home. I search
every dusted-over corner, every bloodstained
diary page, every squinty-eyed photograph
where I am still young enough to be held
without fear of how a tight grip on my arm
would engrave me—what sort of bruise
would be made when the flash blinds us.

What is it that I lost? Was it time? My prime?
A certain kind of love that only happens once,
though we try our best to replicate a counterfeit?

Or just something to believe?

It happened so fast. A switch flipped and I felt
a strange becoming. A flip of the stomach, some
funny churn, and then a pit, a cavern of dread.

If only it left a trail of breadcrumbs. A cryptic
love note. A shape in the cushion, still warm.

Daily Bread

It seems as if

I am forgetting how to be gentle

how to be less madness, more

lavender wick candles, farm-fresh eggs, dog-eared pages of leather-covered Bibles, newborn kittens, off-key Christmas Eve carolers, dimpled baby hands wrapping around larger pinky fingers, chocolate chip brownie batter, past-midnight waltzing under overhead kitchen lights, country homes with front porch swings, weeping willow trees, migrating swarms of monarchs, city cats peering out of city windows, calm of a raging late-August thunderstorm, memorized prayer, first touches shared by new lovers, good news brought to hospital waiting rooms, successful surgeries, first tubes of mascara for the middle-school girls desperate to grow up, every constellation newly discovered by ancient telescope, grass-stained knees on patchwork jeans, the first-ever memory I can recall, rom-com happy endings, the perfect fit of a thrifted prom dress, handmade friendship bracelets I kept on in the chlorinated pool, childhood family vacations, reminders that you love me scrawled on Post-It notes, worn out teddy bears put through the wringer of time, waxing and waning moons, the will to every way, proof of miracles, Mom's apple pie, every delicious summer.

Take me back home

to these small definitions of tenderness

in a mad, mad world.

There

I am too easily overcome. This soul
is inclined to aching, my constitution
worlds away from tenderness. When I try
to envision relief it arrives in phantoms
of something not yet known to me—
a mental picture of a place I've never been.
Imagine it with me, for only a moment,
won't you dare? Reach out, touch it,
feel the fabric between your fingers—

there. I am not being torn at the seams,
there—the stitching holds, the core
within never spills. There is a world
in which I do not wait for the wounds
to stop weeping. It is a world in which
the wounds were never born to begin
with. *There*—my knees do not think
of hitting the floor. Nothing falls
from my eyes. I am only weak

from dreaming easy dreams—

the only trace of weakness I know.

These Days

I tell people *I grew tire♦ of feeling,*
so I ♦eci♦e♦ to stop. Just like that.
Cut the melodrama. I have matters
to tend to. Weeds to pull, papers
to write. No capacity for mourning,
no time to process, no mental space
for any kind of earth-shattering emotion.
I'♦ like to or♦er a blank slate, please,
I bargained with the universe one night,
so apparently, this is just how I live now.
I just wake up each day and promise
to keep composure. I can control the flux.
I am my own government.

A new law: nothing can seep into my skin
if I don't touch it. It's that simple.

But it's impossible for me to move
and not be moved. This I realized
as I watched probably the thousandth
sunset of my life bleed into the horizon
and felt its colors seeping into me, too.

VI

RECLAMATION

I Am Writing to Tell You

That I have learned to accept that good things exist

although I know that in your head I am a cynic
cursing our old friends and letting go of the wheel
forcing fate to pick what comes next. And I know
that *whiplash* and *fury* are the images of me you've kept
and that you remember the ease of which I drained
bottles and bawled the torment out of my lungs
from the balcony and how they almost called the cops
before you took me back to your place and rocked
me to sleep because I couldn't do it on my own

but I am writing to tell you

that I haven't screamed in months and instead
I write poems about August and paint landscapes
of the Rockies although I've never been and now
I take my medicine and pour my life into letters
that I send across the country and I only think
about you when it rains and never out of spite

I am writing to tell you

that I am getting a dog soon and last week I cut my hair
like I do when someone breaks my heart except this time
no one did, I think I just like change now

which I know is foreign to you because back then

you watched me give myself bruises when he decided
he couldn't handle my anger and made me walk home
alone and how afterwards I made you burn my journals
because I couldn't stand seeing that life on paper

I don't want to die anymore

and I don't think you ever met this version of me

in the three years I've loved you and I wonder

if you are still the most tender person in the universe
like I remember you, holding my hair back
from sinking into the toilet water and weeping
with me when I'd talk about the frozen river
under the bridge and how I wanted to marry it

I am writing to tell you

that right now I am eating leftover Chinese food
because I don't hate the way I look in pictures anymore
and that yesterday I spun around in the satin slip I wore
the night of my birthday when you called me a goddess
and how I punched you in the stomach, my little liar,
I wanted to hate you for making me love myself

but I am writing to tell you

that I do now.

I grip the wheel.

I am good to my body.

I want to live.

I Find My Power

in the way
the azalea bush in my front yard
never asked for permission to bloom,
it just did.

If Eve Were Not of Eden

I imagine she'd *talk back bleach her hair cry to records that skip.*
Would she *wear ripped jeans love the wrong boy ruin the right one?*
If Eve didn't earn her fame for plucking forbidden fruit I imagine
she'd be wicked good company. She'd be all *60 in a 45 windows*
down blasting the profane music. Eve would *giggle at all the sick jokes*
read all the censored books do it all without batting an eyelash.
If Eve were not of Adam would we care for her at all?
If she were less stolen rib and more *flammable woman?*
If Eve were not the doer of damnation, the action cursed,
the forever receiver of our shaking fists, I imagine
I might adore her, *to be brave enough to risk perfection*
for freedom, to be bigger than the garden,
than even knowledge, to be bold enough
to reach and pull.

If Eve were not of Eden I imagine
she'd be everything I'd love to be.

An Amalgamation of Sweet Nothings

or: these small things I love will carry me through

your Saturday morning bedhead, eyes still sticky with sleep / the realism
of my childhood fiction / lemongrass on the first day of May / the satisfaction of a perfect origami crease / John Denver's *Poems, Prayers &
Promises* swelling in the air / ancient snowglobe collections blanketed by
a thin layer of dust / dead hopes of loving the wrong person that don't
haunt me anymore / a dog-eared, years-loved paperback of *Frankenstein* /
dimpled babies with full lifetimes brimming ahead of them / storms that
leave us restless / pressed azaleas tucked neatly into white envelopes to
travel long distances / the strange texture of lavender petroleum jelly / a
hot drink burning all the way down / the mere idea of expensive French
cheese and wine to accompany it / native wildflowers and local honey /
piles of half-full journals and forever-unfinished scrapbooks / how I can't
quite turn any of this to poetry, but / that I still try /

Self-Portrait, 20

These days I don't hate myself like I used to or even at all. I am all chapped lips and split ends and unpainted fingernails because by now I've learned I always chip them within hours anyway. A few weeks ago I got my mom to box-dye my hair *Intense Black* like it used to look before one too many crisis experiments with scissors and bleach. I've been trying to get back to my roots, so to speak. By roots I mean I'm just trying to find the same shade of *happy* that used to color my world as a girl. I've had no luck trying to find it in Home Depot paint samples or lipstick hues or other eyes so maybe I'll stumble upon it somewhere inside my own. I've even let myself believe in God again. That's been going well. There is poetry in the Bible and past midnight when I teach my lips to muscle-memory the prayers. Usually, though, I just end up rambling to Him about wintertime in the mountains or my best friend's smile when he meets me in the morning or how sometimes my separation anxiety is so bad I feel like I'm still the same kindergartner who cried for hours in the guidance counselor's cluttered office. It's as if I never outgrew that wide-eyed state of needing to feel tended to. I've been trying to drill the word *enough* into my head. I have enough beauty and enough time and enough love in my heart to keep the world from dying. And strangely enough, it's working.

Visions of Eden

after Joni Mitchell's "Woo•stock"

Bathed in sunlight, I feel almost human.
Must be the antidote to my strangeness,
spine melting into wet soil, facing the ether.
How strange it is to inhabit a body, mortal
stardust, cosmic temple. Nothing earthly
has ever eased me. But there is a feeling like
coming home or *holiness* or *•ivinity* when
my bones are clothed by warmth. To feel
seen by the sky, pursued by its glow, how
it overcomes me. *Remember that you are*
star•ust an• to star•ust you shall return.
The infinite calls me Child. Endlessness
breathes my name and I listen, obedient.

To the Dreamer That Will One Day Be My Daughter

I.
When you are still a bug-eyed,
sticky-fingered believer of everything,
I will teach you words.
I will let your tiny cushioned index finger
trace the darkened letters
of poetry you will not understand
for years to come, for now
just shapes and sounds and
the rustle of your baby hands
eager for the next page.
You will learn to be eager.
You, dimpled and smooth, will learn
to always finish your sentences.

II.
I will teach you defiance.
You'll tiptoe down the stairs
in my tallest heels, fairy
wings from Halloween, tangled
hair and cheeks stained
with magic markers.
Messy, my baby, is beautiful.
And from the kitchen window
I will watch you spinning on the lawn,
entranced by the winds of your own

imagination.
And when the fresh-faced little girls
in ironed dresses and pristine
patent leather shoes
point and taunt and giggle
at your dizzy singing,
I will smile over the dishes.
This is the moment we both realize
the world will never understand
girls like you.

But you,
tooth missing and shoulders
burnt, keep spinning, because
"sorry" is the only word
I will never teach you.

III.
When a boy (or girl) dares
to white-knuckle your heart
for the first time, I will let you cry.
I will let your fury burn holes
into your childhood pillowcase, your
frame warming the mattress as you learn
that loss sometimes means sleeping
through the afternoon.
When you feel more human,
more goddess, more fire,
we will drive with no intended destination
until the sky burns blood orange
and the water towers do not know us
by name. Escape, my love.
Even the greatest warriors
must breathe.

But when we come back home,
drunk on fresh mountain air,
like the sky, you must burn.
Burn—
every notion that they took
anything from you, a sliver
of your soul, even a
drop of your spirit. Burn—
until black smoke clouds
lead you back into your mother's arms.

There is no way to silence the girl
who was taught to finish her sentences.

She will always be
half poetry,
half me.

Life Moves Above Awareness

I am thinking of the things we leave behind before we even have the chance to notice. Skin cells and soulmates and stories. Strands of loose hair in the shower, fingerprints on escalator handrails, shot glances, minor details of our histories *(what you ate for breakfast on your first day of sixth grade)*, these small things of which we do not care enough to store for safekeeping. Life moves above awareness and permanence is only as permanent as it feels. This I know because there came a day I found myself standing very still in the middle of a bustling sidewalk stranded in a city, a moment, a life I could not recognize. The natural question came to mind: *How did I get here?* as I stood in a body unknown to me, alien vessel drowning in a sea of colors I could not name. Sensory overload, system failure, panic. Cars drove past without noticing, time still set in motion with no regard for who chooses to stand motionless. It hit me then and there, in the eye of my own hurricane, that everything I shed—hair ties left behind on ex-boyfriends' nightstands, poems written on the backs of coffee shop napkins crumpled and tossed into train station garbage cans, an old phone number saved in a dead friend's phone—took me here. It was all my doing. Every act unnoticed is still an act after all.

Cures for Being

Turn off the news. Nothing good ever stemmed from analysis. Tune out the affairs of this time, the intoxicating stream of *coul* *be* and *what if*. Hardly matters who's nuking who. Hardly matters what the weather will bring. Just dress for anything, preferably waterproof. Pack lightly but always carry an umbrella. Allow yourself the pleasure of becoming a garden. You have all the privilege you need to survive if you root yourself in the choice of joy and let yourself get rained on. You are a living meadow. I wish I had learned this when I was young. I would have saved myself twenty years of anger. I would have saved myself from headlines, from flash floods, from analysis.

Praise to the Holy Habitual

The story goes like this.

One day you're sitting in a living room on a Friday night
with the family you chose for yourself, howling laughter
ricocheting off apartment walls, everyone seeing double.
We're fifteen bodies content in perfect company, pushing
the limits of a noise complaint from the neighbors, but
singing out anyway, because *we are here, we are here*

and then we're not

and we may never be again

at least not in the same way.

Perfect configurations, these habitual moments
we hold close but never quite close enough.

For a brief moment in time we were just twenty-somethings
kicking our shoes off by the door to stay for a while.

That's the story.

It has no ending

but maybe that's what makes it worth telling.

We were there,

we were there,

we were there.

I could sing it out forever.

Tunnel Vision

When the movie of my life plays before my eyes, a recap of however many years I've collected, when I'm clinging onto the skin of it by a thinning thread and the faint music hums in that near-death glimmer of a blinding light, I wonder what I'll see. The other night I wept over the idea, living tears burning my body, one day gone, this temporary vessel. What will be my final vision, passing from this world to whatever cryptic life (or lack thereof) exists apart from this one? Who will be waiting for me at the finish line, holding a poster? What will it say?

I've been too many people for too many people. I've played hero and villain and wounded thing crouching in the corner of a bad man's bedroom. I've played the other woman and your only woman and the shivering woman, dipping her toe into the frigid waters of an unknown river, half-alive and tempted to drown.

Maybe, in that long-awaited slideshow of memory, I'll greet every great love of my life again, every pair of eyes I've adored, lingering for a brief moment just to warm myself by those familiar fires. I'm a lucky one. I've been seen by so many.

I'll watch myself break and bloom all over again. There's no use crying now.

When I reach God, in all of his unfathomable might, he'll smile and ask me, "How did you like your life?" and I'll look down and whisper, "Which one?"

I Like It Here

Where sheep graze lazily
around the sunset-stained silo across our street.
I live in a world fit for a stamped postcard,
wild purple berries lining the valley paths
and tree-covered hideaways, where stillness
is not only allowed but encouraged.
Nothing is demanded of the farmland wanderer,
perfumed by morning dew and inebriated
by the gentleness of a dying August.
I like it here, where the wild river twists
in its rugged beauty, where the sky breaks
open enough for me to hear my heartbeat
singing *I am alive, I am alive,*
I know I am alive.

Open Letter to Seventeen

I know you're convinced this world would not miss you. But I'm sending you this letter through the space-time continuum equivalent of the USPS (*sad story about that, actually, but we'll get there*) aiming to persuade you otherwise. One day you'll be twenty (*weird, right?*) and you'll have your own apartment where you'll keep unlit vanilla candles by the windowsill and a boyfriend (*!!!*) who adores long, pensive walks to nowhere as much as you do. You'll be able to cook for yourself (*no, not Michelin star worthy, but at least you'll be able to fry a mean egg*) and set up your own therapy appointments (*you'll tremble through it, but that's alright*) and keep real friends around for Friday night shenanigans and Saturday morning recovery breakfasts. I know you hate the idea of having friends. That you've accepted your role as forever wallflower, the disposable stand-in at everyone's parade, perpetually the girl who escaped high school homecoming to cry in the parking lot, hot tears glittering in her palms. But I'm writing to tell you that you're graduating college next year (*yes, already... but right now you're living through a dark time in history. I'll spare you the details, but you're gonna be just fine*) and that you wear real perfume and have stopped dyeing your hair drugstore blonde because, let's face it, it's always looked strange. State of the union: you still grind your teeth. You have crippling back pain now and you've got the eyesight of a centenarian. But you have enough conviction now to call yourself a capital-P Poet, and you say *yes* to the things that scare you and *yes*, love, this world would miss you (*terribly*).

Portrait of Eve

after Jorie Graham, Sylvia Plath

I understand you now. The gesture, too.
You just wanted something to sink your teeth into.

And so you plucked. The bough frowned.
So did God. And Adam, still unseeing, felt something in him crumple.

The fabric of the universe wrinkled. The veil of time tore in two.
Before and after. Before you plucked, after you tasted.

How sweet this song of womankind.
Eternity bores me,
I never wante it.*

Skin torn, letting the juice drip to the elbows.
How apple-crisp is rebellion, that chewing and swallowing of freedom?

I get it, beautiful sister of mine.
You had your eye on it from the moment it began growing.
It's what we do best, giving nothing up.

But giving,
for eternity, in.

To Be Born Woman

does not mean to exist
in a state of perpetual delicacy.

It is not in my design to walk
in constant tiptoe, careful
not to upset the creaking floorboards,
not to shatter your fallen eggshells.
I was not built to stand with a spine
made of mother's finest china, a heart of silk
that could tear with the wrong kind of tug.

Because my softness is far from weakness.

I will love you with a gentle touch, and
with words that, when whispered, will travel
to the marrow of your bones, and stay there,
taking off their shoes, building a home in that place.

I will even light a fire there, preparing the kindling,
fanning the flames with my breath alone, letting
the smoldering embers waltz in the air, knowing
I am the wind that keeps you alive.

It's just what we do.

We are both the act of burning
and precisely what you burn for.

Scenic Views From Center Stage

I will not fade into the backdrop of my life.
I beg of you, do not insult these restless dreams
by holding them against theatrical scenery. I am
no prop, no stunning recreation of Shakespeare's
iconic balcony scene. Do not compare my body
to fake ivy snaking around the makeshift lattice.

This is refusal. Mark my words. I will not play
supporting actress on the stage I built myself.

Draw the curtains. This is my show. Let me
play spectacle, the star far outshining those
blinding overhead lights. Start the sound
check. I'll wait for the violins to cue me in.

I will not fade into the backdrop of my life.
I will glitter and glow. I hardly care if you
show up or not. The show must go on
with or without you, receiving or lacking
the standing ovation I earned on my own.

Lessons From a Butterfly

Consider the monarch.

She only lives for herself,
as flighty and elusive as she desires.
Ungoverned and unrestrained, she soars
without seeking permission to do so.

I admit, I could learn a lot from her—
like how to flee when the season has ended,
how to migrate thousands of miles away
from bitterness, how to taste like poison,
how to settle elsewhere and not look back.

Mostly though, how to be that bold.
A fluttering, wild, brutal thing.
How to be weightless enough
to still be carried by wind,
how to be heavy enough
to not get carried away.

Quietudes

from my chil♦hoo♦ neighborhoo♦

Bathed in blushing light, I do not dwell
upon death for the first time in weeks.
Instead, I let the atoms of my body
make cosmic love to the sidewalk shadows,
a strange sensation of fulfillment soaring
past the treetops of this miniature world.
I welcome it—these rare quietudes—
where I can lay my armor down
and think of nothing else beyond
the forgiveness of sun
on living skin.

Stretch Marks

are
winding roads,
proof of survival,
scars from won battles,
fresh paint on canvas,
free tattoos,
evidence of outgrowing,
poetic transformation,
stories worth telling,
the body's way of healing,
of making space for more,
the meaning of resilience,
unfinished timelines,
cirrus clouds,
billowing smoke,
shed feathers,
scenic routes,
flyaway hairs,
wear and tear,
graffiti murals,
delicate boldness,
torn veils,
the aftermath of motion,
rips in the fabric of the universe,
a child's cursive,
shooting stars,
the constellations
I follow home.

The Language of Spring

This is the season for falling in love.

That's what the dogwoods whispered
this morning when I walked by, musing,
their white petals unfolding in the April wind.

I almost refused to believe them,
those shy voices branching into endless sky.
Because after the winter we just survived,
what is left to believe in?

And then I understood.

The chirp of hummingbirds, the rush of the creek,
the children playing under a sun that warms
but does not yet burn. A faint scent of magnolia.
Everything awakening, buzzing: an evening sky
ablaze, the flight of the honeybee, a trail of roses
scattered along sidewalk paths meant for wandering.
And I, aimless dreamer, blushing all the way home.

This, here, is something special.

Some sort of prayer.

Something worth believing in.

Citizens of Beauty

I pledge allegiance
to Octobers in the Blue Ridge,
her autumn air a sincere sort of baptism.
And to the weeping branches of the willow trees
where I sit at the pond and weep over everything
I have given away, leaves fluttering as if they can listen,
as if they are. To the grazing cows, to the noisy streams,
to the orchid skies we melt beneath, our spines engraving
into damp earth, both of us high on petrichor. It is grace
to be a citizen of beauty. To be sons and daughters of
valleys where wildflowers spring in the snow, to be
the dumb and baffled children swept in her seas.
To the fields striped with yellow and the mossy
troves, to the kisses we exchange under paling
moonlight, to the stars that keep our prayers,
I pledge allegiance to you and you alone.

Names and Trees and Variations of God

I like to go for walks around the manmade pond near my apartment complex and take low-quality pictures of the massive weeping willow that looms over the asphalt bike path. I do this solely for the purpose of curating evidence in my camera roll that I am, in fact, still alive. Sometimes I forget. I think that, in a world like ours, forgetting is becoming more and more acceptable. It feels good to forget. Think about it. There eventually comes a day when someone casually brings up a name in conversation—*that* name, you know which one I'm talking about—the name you swore you'd never be able to hear without feeling your insides weaken into gelatin, body crumpling into nothing but blood and guts—and then you realize that the name—*that* name—hasn't crossed your mind all morning for the first time in a handful of hellish months. Forgetting feels a little like religion. Like hearing whoever God is to you, speaking within the innermost chamber of your heart. Forgetting can make you want to write a sappy love letter to the universe: *thank you for setting me free!* Sometimes I forget I am a person who will one day, like every other person who has ever been and will ever be, die. So I go for walks with headphones on, blasting the music of my parents' generation. Sometimes no music at all, just me in my infinite silence, taking photos of the foliage to save for later. These days I like to save some things for myself. I like to remember. I like hearing my name.

Encapsulated

The ocean is a healing rage. Medicinal fury, restorative wrath. I feel connected to the water, knowing it has mingled with the branches of my ancestry. We all wade in the same recycled substance, every life connected by what falls from the heavens. Water is a cyclical being, prone to temper tantrums, almost too easily offended. I, too, am turbulent. I live forever misunderstood. Maybe this is why, running haphazardly and barefoot into the deep, I am overcome by a coming-home sort of feeling, fully known, where I do not have to pretend I am anything but a buoyant body, calm at long last. The ocean understands. We speak the same mother tongue, back and forth in crashing waves, tender darkness.

Visions of a Life

That feeling—a nighttime walk in the crepuscular light
of late November, leaves crunching under rain boots
I wore by accident, having misunderstood the forecast
while rushing to catch the late bus in the morning.

There's a certain kind of magic in *that kin* of being alone,
wandering home at half past seven, taking the longer route
just to bask in the breeze for a moment more. It's hard not
to peer through the golden windows of other people's
homes without appearing freakish and unnatural. But I do

anyway, sometimes, as they fold their laundry or put away
dinner plates or chat with their mothers on the phone.
Sometimes I'm lucky enough to catch a warm embrace
shared under the kitchen light fixtures. Sometimes I don't
catch anything at all, just a dim room and a cat perched
on the ledge. A messy desk. An unwatered houseplant.

There's a fondness in feeling momentarily at home in the world.

Periphery

When I blur away the countryside, sixty-five miles per hour shuttling through the Shenandoah Valley, everything feels right again. There's something potent about living on the fringes of things. From the backseat window I reduce the world to color, lines of dairy cows merely black and white brushstrokes decorating a living green canvas, all scenery rushing before my eyes converted to watercolor. It's much safer to inhabit a place like this. No one has anything to say, nothing to purge nor wield. In this place no language is necessary, for there is no real life here, only pigments colliding with loose shapes, edges bending and lacking, my own dizzy mayhem. How I adore this incomprehensible movement. Here the world spills into itself. No one stops it from doing so. Today I'm heading home and it feels right. I've got The Four Seasons' "Can't Take My Eyes Off You" melting my brain to candle wax, daydreams as pliable as modeling clay, and cumulus clouds hanging above me as unapologetic as ever, specially designed for getting lost in.

Do Not Let Me Run

so fast I forget to absorb the *now now now* of being where my feet are. I refuse to reduce these years to blurred half-truths and half-asleep rainy mornings I spend on the nauseating bus humming down Prices Fork Road. I want to remember the stickiness of the rain here, even in the bitter cold mud of the New River Valley where everything ironically feels old, nothing *new* at all, the very soil we stand on worked by human hands deeper than anywhere I've ever been rooted. Do not let me forget the electricity of this place. How holy the fog on a Sunday morning, how charged the stars every night I stumble home in the dizzy glory of a twenty-something dreamer. Do not let me call these open fields anything but home, these cornfield paths, the jagged and unexpected trails left behind by speeding bicycles cutting through the farmland, the sheer audacity of the springtime to be this tender on the soul, and the silent horses stopping to observe us as we pass, thinking of nothing but the kindness of our company.

Layers

To be born a creature constantly evolving
is a God-given grace I do not deserve

but one I savor with every fiber
of my being, to be made of layers,
to be allowed the gift of unraveling.

As if no matter how much of me this world
takes and takes and takes, whether it be
the strength from my spine or the flush
of my face when it finds yours among many
in a crowded room, no matter if everything
I hold is stolen from my hands, cupped
in prayer, no matter if I am left with nothing,

I will never truly be left with nothing.

I will always have poetry.

And layers.

And you.

Today I Give Thanks for Simply Being

A Villanelle

Today I give thanks for simply being.
For words, for hands that hold mine too tightly.
Listen now—you can hear my heart speaking.

How I hope this joy is far from fleeting.
I have never before loved this brightly.
Today I give thanks for simply being.

I cherish my soul, all of its feeling.
Though sometimes I know I must tread lightly.
Listen now—you can hear my heart speaking.

Do you hear that, the sound of it beating?
It drums, it sings, and never politely.
Today I give thanks for simply being.

All of life is just hiding and seeking.
For love, for poetry flowing nightly.
Listen now—you can hear my heart speaking.

It is an art, to focus on breathing.
Nothing less or more, in and out blindly.
Today I give thanks for simply being.
Listen now—you can hear my heart speaking.

Life Does Not End at Its Ending

Rather—we are steadily finishing
in junctures unknown to us, little
by little giving away more and more.
Consider the transfiguration of shed skin
into dust. Or a lover breathing steadily
in their sleep, thawing your bones in the dead
of winter, how you never predict the finale
of a season until it arrives and they depart.
Time reconstructs, unfastens its buttons,
unwinds until the thread is spent. Time is
the art of losing what cannot earn its keep.
And I, hostage to its clutches, am trying
to notice these quiet slippings, these unseen
losses. This morning I noted that the hydrangeas
clinging to the wooden fence of my childhood
home have been drained of color. It is clear
I am not trying hard enough. What else drips
through the spaces between my fingers?
Which parts of us are already coming undone?

Silly Little Life

Plants, half-alive, guard my bedroom like soldiers
on my apartment windowsill. I have short hair now
and wear extra-large sweaters because they're comfier
than the kind in my actual size and I have given up
on giving up my comfort for anyone. An abbreviated
list of recent obsessions: a full moon on a cloudless night,
mango peach-flavored anything, fifty-cent mini pumpkins
at the grocery store on Saturday mornings. I am both
wise and foolish, the contradiction of calling oneself
a jaded optimist. Something you might not know
about me is that I've spent most of my life wanting
nothing more than to die. But I am writing this now
and it's finally October of the worst year of everyone's
life, and the leaves are starting to turn and I'm a month
from twenty-one. I track the moon cycles on my phone.
I can keep succulents alive—so far, at least. I'm the star
of baking chocolate banana bread with my roommates
and watching *How I Met Your Mother* with my sweet boy
for *only God knows how many* consecutive times now
and I think I like living this silly little life, I really do.

Beyond Even Blood

I am marrow and carbon and the blues.

There's a poem in me somewhere.

[Nothing to find tucked in the crease of my elbow or behind my ears where I secure overgrown bangs from falling into my eyes or even the soft dip of my lower back tailor-made for tenderness. I have searched for it on the backs of my eyelids, the fleshy interior side of my lower lip, a manhunt for words engraved under my nail beds—]

I am fiber and plasma and the scattered aftermath of a supernova.

I am a reservoir for water and heartache and less blood than you'd think. I used to think we were mostly blood. I looked it up and we're not. We're only 7% of it. This is why blood is sacred.

Beyond half-functioning organs, a bad spine, beyond birthmarks and scars from a childhood of anger,

[somewhere, invisible to the naked eye, a poem shifts in its sleep—]

My Heart Hoards It All

I water dead plants and store volumes of love letters from five years ago and keep ticket stubs from mediocre movies I saw with friends who hate me now. It's in my nature, I think, to cling to futility. I joke sometimes that I've never gotten over anything, *ever*. That everything I've ever loved will always be loved even when it is no longer encouraged or even allowed. My friends think I've gone mad. I scrapbook memories much like mothers do with their babies' firsts. First steps, first solid foods, first words. Except mine consist less of beginnings and more of endings. My heart hoards it all. The prom dress that doesn't fit me anymore, college rejection letters from ages past, the final photo I took with my childhood crush before he died. Maybe I *have* gone mad, or maybe this is just my way of loving. Archiving the shopping receipts. Pressing flowers from old flames. And of course, watering the plants until the soil spills over the edge.

Meandering

after Mitski, "Francis Forever"

I'm begging God to slow time. Drag the clock, please; curb my insatiable appetite for speed. I've been beseeching the universe to make me painfully aware of every small moment slipping between my fingers before they're all gone for good. Seasons pass without warning or indication and *I'm not rea♦y for the en♦ of this one.* There is a finite space between every dawn and dusk. Every birth and death. Every departure and destination. Only until it is gone do we realize the significance of the *going.* I *shoul♦ have* loved you more if I knew I'd have to stop one day. I *shoul♦ have* admired the autumn for a few more afternoons before the bright orange skyline would inevitably fade. I *shoul♦ have* savored the present. Held more hands. Kissed deeper. Melted over the sweet nothings: precious company, full tables, easy conversation. Expressed my care. Spoken up. Said what I wanted to say but never did, the words spilling out without walls.

A prayer.

Let me get there gradually. Let me let it all go, piece by piece and unhurried, without the blunt sensation of being ripped out of a safe womb. Let it be a steady goodbye—a slow burn, a softer pain.

There Is So Much Comfort
in Knowing

that what I hold closest to me
cannot be taken away.

And no, it is not another body
this time, (or any time, really)–

despite the changing seasons
(they arrive more rapid-fire now,
these days more noticeable)

there is one thing that remains
as constant as earth, as rooted
as the branches of my family tree,
as fixed as the sepia-toned ancestors
that hang from the wall in all
of their foreign strangeness:

it is this *con•ition*
of being more fire than girl
more distant artist than reliable friend
more often chasing the fever dream
than sitting still with the reality
that I should.

I love that nothing
can steal this from me, this
wild woman magic I write

and carry and spill and bleed
and gift and ruin and become

only for hands that
are deserving to hold this

uncharted, wounded animal
I am

so much
you cannot take,

I am.

Today I Am Not an Open Wound

but a poem.

Something blooming, all peony pink
and fresh-petaled, swaying in the sweetness of it all.
I am bubbles rising from soapy wands, less April shower
and more April *symphony:* what a way to blossom this is,
this springing (not falling) in love again,
this simple joy of praying to be picked.

Today I am not an open wound

but I used to be.

And I thank these clear skies for that ancient history of mine.
For crumpling on bathroom floors and breaking in stalls,
for yellow, tender bruises, for the wrong love.
I say thank you to the torrential downpour
of *too much girl, never enough reasons to stay.*

Today I'll put on a record, a love letter to the universe.
It's broken. It skips. I play it anyway. I even sing.

thank you, thank you, thank you—

for taking from me what I thought
I could not live without

thank you, thank you, thank you—

for more space to dance.

I Will Not Go Gentle

after Dylan Thomas

I will not go gentle

into any good night. This body
loves its rage. I will not sit back
for any show. When it comes time
to depart I will do it with a throat
sore from screaming. Bruised knees
and fingertips charred from toying
with embers. I will not submit
to the silence of slipping away.
I will leave with bloodshot eyes
and shattered bones. Skin torn
from having lived a life of feeling.
I will not leave before letting
the whole world know *I was here.*
I was here. I was here and to be me

was to make sure of it. I will not
leave under cover of darkness.
I will leave an echo. A porch light.
A poem. I will leave my love on.

Acknowledgements

Too many people to thank.

For starters:

My parents, Jose and Mylene Garcia—for pushing me to write, to be fearless in the pursuit of my passions, and for quite literally creating me (you're cool for that, by the way!) Everything I do is for both of you. I am proud to be the only daughter of two remarkable, resilient, and devoted people who have exemplified unconditional love since the day I was born.

My family—the cousins (practically siblings!) I grew up down the street from, the faraway ones and the others I still have yet to meet, the grandparents I take after in ways I'll never fully know, the dead and the living, and every tradition we've passed down through generations. I will keep telling my stories for as long as I'm able. They're your stories, too.

My chosen family—my cherished childhood friends in Lake Ridge, my beautiful and brilliant college friends in Blacksburg, my pen pals scattered throughout the world, those who have supported me online, in my local communities, and in all of the places I've been privileged enough to call home. You saved my life in infinite ways.

My sweet love—you know who you are. You're a bit camera shy, and maybe you're paper shy, too, so I'll just let you find this and *know*. I love you beyond poetry and distance and time. Thank you for doing life with me. I like mine a billion times more with you in it.

My teachers and professors—the ones that first noticed the electric spark for writing I carried with me as a young girl, the ones who implored me to take every opportunity to chase my voice, and especially the ones who extended a hand of criticism—for your kindness I am eternally grateful.

MICHELLE EMILY GARCIA IS A TWENTY-ONE-YEAR-OLD POET, MEMOIRIST, AND MULTIMEDIA ARTIST.

Hailing from Lake Ridge, Virginia, Michelle is a third-year senior at Virginia Polytechnic Institute & State University in Blacksburg, Virginia, where she studies English Literature & Language, Creative Writing, and Communication Science & Social Inquiry. Michelle will graduate summa cum laude in May 2021 with dual Bachelor of Arts degrees. *Cul-*‌*e-sac Angels* is her solo debut publication.

Michelle's work has been recognized by the Scholastic Art & Writing Awards in the D.C. Metro region, receiving multiple awards throughout her time at Woodbridge Senior High School (Class of 2018). Her work has been published in various editions of *E**‌*as* (WSHS) and *Silhouette* (VT) literary magazines. In 2020, she was featured as a local artist and innovator by PW Perspective, a media publication focused on showcasing the diverse voices of Prince William County, Virginia. In the same year, a collection of Michelle's poetry written during the COVID-19 pandemic was published in *Mim Magazine*. She was recognized as a top 10 finalist for the Giovanni-Steger Poetry Prize of Virginia Tech in the spring of 2021, and her senior thesis on the Brontë sisters will be published in *Philologia,* Virginia Tech's undergraduate research journal for the College of Liberal Arts and Human Sciences.